Radioactive Tracer Techniques

BY

GEO. K. SCHWEITZER

Assistant Professor of Chemistry,
University of Tennessee

AND

IRA B. WHITNEY

Chief Supervisor,
Radio Chemical Process Development,
Oak Ridge National Laboratories

D. VAN NOSTRAND COMPANY, INC.

TORONTO   NEW YORK   LONDON

NEW YORK

D. Van Nostrand Company, Inc., 250 Fourth Avenue, New York 3

TORONTO

D. Van Nostrand Company (Canada), Ltd., 228 Bloor Street, Toronto

LONDON

Macmillan & Company, Ltd., St. Martin's Street, London, W.C. 2

PRINTED IN THE UNITED STATES OF AMERICA

PREFACE

This manual is designed to serve as a guide for laboratory work and instruction in the utilization of radioactive tracers. The amazing strides made in recent years in this field have impressed every scientist with the value of these research tools. The major barrier to the use of radiotracers has been a lack of knowledge concerning the techniques involved. An attempt has been made herein to provide such instruction in the form of a compact presentation.

The first four chapters of the book are fundamental because they deal with topics pertinent to all radioactive laboratory work. The reader should familiarize himself thoroughly with this material before any experimental work is attempted. Special attention should be given to the sections discussing safety precautions.

Basic experiments are presented in chapter 5. This division contains seven experiments dealing with the methods and peculiarities of radioactivity measurements and properties of radioactive substances. The remainder of the book is devoted to material illustrating chemical, physical and biological tracer methods. The final chapter discusses special preparations. An appendix of general information is provided also.

The experiments have been planned so that they require only the most readily available radioactive materials. The necessity for the preparation of special radioactive solutions has been held to a minimum.

The following chart may be used as a guide to the selection of experiments:

Type	Duration	Suggested Experiments
Radiochemistry	12 5-hr. periods	1, 2, 3, 4, 5, 6, 7, 8, 10, 12, 18, 25
Radiochemistry	15 5-hr. periods	1, 2, 3, 4, 5, 6, 7, 8, 10, 11, 12, 14, 18, 23, 25
Radiobiology	12 5-hr. periods	1, 2, 3, 4, 5, 6, 9, 17, 25, 26, 27, 28
Radiobiology	15 5-hr. periods	1, 2, 3, 4, 5, 6, 7, 8, 9, 12, 17, 25, 26, 27, 28
Radiophysics	12 5-hr. periods	1, 2, 3, 4, 5, 9, 16, 17, 18, 22, 24, 25
Radiophysics	15 5-hr. periods	1, 2, 3, 4, 5, 6, 9, 16, 17, 18, 20 or 21, 22, 23, 24, 25
Radiotracers for Engineers	12 5-hr. periods	1, 2, 3, 4, 5, 10, 13, 15, 16, 17, 22, 25

The writers wish to thank the following people for assistance in preparation of the manuscript: Mr. Logan B. Emlet, Dr. H. A. Levy, Dr. K. Z. Morgan, and Dr. P. C. Tompkins of Oak Ridge National Laboratories, and Dr. C. L. Comar and Dr. H. A. Smith of the University of Tennessee.

This work is a pioneer in the field. Corrections, criticism, and ideas for future editions are invited.

G. K. S.
I. B. W.

Oak Ridge, Tennessee
April, 1949

CONTENTS

v

Chapter I

RADIOACTIVE HAZARDS

RADIOACTIVE HAZARDS

Introduction. The use of radioactive materials in the laboratory is not new to the scientist. Ever since Madame Curie isolated radium and polonium, radioactive substances have been studied. However, since the advent of the atomic bomb and the subsequent release of relatively large amounts of induced radioactive elements by the United States Atomic Energy Commission (A. E. C.), the use of these materials has become more widespread than ever before. Considering the distribution of radioactive substances, very little practical information concerning their handling in tracer quantities has been published. A few articles that have been written relate the experience of experts and enumerate rules for "hot"[1] laboratories. These articles consider radioactivity from the viewpoint of the A. E. C. laboratories which are concerned primarily with large amounts of active substances. The problems encountered in those laboratories are far more complex than any that may be found in the laboratory concerned with teaching students the basic principles involved in the safe handling of radioactivity.

As has been emphasized by the A. E. C. writers, safety in the radiochemical laboratory is of prime importance. Health hazards, such as the radioactive contamination of the body and external and internal exposure to radioactive materials, are the most important problems to those who

---

[1] Hot laboratories are laboratories handling millicurie to curie amounts of substances.

will use radioisotopes in the laboratory, in medicine, or in industry. Contamination must be considered wherever radioactive substances are used. The laboratory desks, hoods, floors, or anything that is used to handle radioisotopes and other parts of the laboratory that indirectly contact these materials may become contaminated and thereby become a health hazard to the laboratory personnel. Persons dealing with radioactivity must be vigilant at all times in order to prevent the spreading of activity. Unless this is done the laboratory will become so badly contaminated that the room will have to be abandoned because of the radiation hazards or because accurate work will be impossible in the presence of the high background activity.

Contamination. The word contamination will be used and heard many times by those who handle radioactive materials. The word may become repugnant to many because of the apparent overuse. No matter how many times it is used or heard, the word, "contamination," and all that it means must never be forgotten by those working with radioisotopes.

The first articles in the laboratory that receive radioactivity will usually be the glass equipment used in an experiment. From the moment the first drop of "active" liquid or solid is transferred from the original shipping container until the end of the experiment, the operator must consider each successive piece of equipment as being contaminated, at least until it is proven otherwise. Since only minute quantities of activity are used in tracer studies, it becomes highly important that all traces be removed from the equipment before reuse. If this is not done, an experiment may be completely ruined by having the contaminating activity concentrate in a different fraction or in the same fraction as the isotope that is being studied.

The equipment used in an experiment becomes one of the best agents for the contamination of the laboratory in general. There may be "active" solution on the outer surface which will be transferred to the laboratory bench or the hands of the manipulator. If active material gets on the hands, whatever is touched thereafter will become contaminated and acts as a hazard to the next person who uses the laboratory. Therefore, it becomes necessary to place all contaminated equipment in special receptacles or at certain designated places in the laboratory.

Various laboratory operations may be the cause of contaminating large areas of hoods, benches, or floors unless the operator has thought through the experiment beforehand. These operations are: evaporations of solutions containing normally volatile "active" constituents, such as iodine; evaporations in general, since spray that is carried from a boiling solution will always carry nonvolatile activity; crystallizations or evaporations to dryness with resultant spattering or bumping; transfers of liquid by pipette or pouring; and others which the student will readily recognize.

Not only the laboratory but also the student himself may become contaminated in the operations as outlined above. He may easily get his hands contaminated and from this source may contaminate the laboratory, his clothes, and any other place he may go. Contamination of the person or his clothes is by far the most dangerous form of contamination. This type of contamination is a health hazard and will be considered in greater detail later.

Methods of Detecting Contamination. Thinking that contamination does not exist in a laboratory is of little value. It must be *known* that contamination does not exist. Thus, instruments that can detect the presence of activity must be provided. At present there are several on the market that can be used to "survey" the laboratory or the personnel in order to detect unwanted activity.[2] These instruments are of various designs but essentially they are all Geiger-Mueller tubes, ionization chambers, or film meters which record either the rate of radiation received on a meter scaled in milliroentgens per hour or the integrated dose in milliroentgens received during the period of exposure.

In order to detect contamination, the portable radiation rate meter is passed slowly over the surface suspected and the recording device is watched for any increase in rate. The exact spot may often be found using these instruments. Needless to say, as soon as any contamination is found, the location is immediately cleaned.

Another method in use in some laboratories is called the smear test. Small filter papers (about three centimeters in diameter) are lightly rubbed over a prescribed area (usually twelve square inches). These papers are then "counted" using a Geiger-Mueller scaler. This method is often useful when personnel are available to count the smears and report the results to the person in charge of the laboratory, the method has its principle merit in indicating the presence of contamination that might be easily spread. However, there are several disadvantages inherent in the method. In the first place, the method is valid only when used by experienced personnel, since the variation of pressure applied during the rubbing of the surface will result in variation of the amount of active material removed and counted. Then the contaminated spot may be only a small fraction of the total area covered by rubbing, thus resulting in a larger area becoming contaminated. Also, it is possible, unless the whole area is contaminated, to miss contaminated spots entirely. And lastly, the act of rubbing

[2] See Appendix for distributors.

the surface may cause dust to rise which will carry with it some active materials which can be inhaled by the laboratory personnel.

Methods of Cleaning. Even under the closest supervision, there will be times when some portion of the laboratory becomes contaminated. Therefore, the student should understand the basic principles involved in removing the hazard. The whole field of decontamination is new and not too well understood. A considerable amount of the knowledge is based entirely on personal experience. However, the chemist has the tools for decontamination, provided he uses sound chemical principles. For instance, one should not try to remove active phosphorus using soaps that will precipitate insoluble phosphates. Also, if active iodine gets on the hands, the use of an oxidizing agent such as permanganate followed by sulfite will effectively remove the activity. In general, the agent that is used to remove the activity should be one which will give the greatest solubility for the contamination. Where strong acids or alkalies can be used, they will serve the best. Metal surfaces can be cleaned rapidly this way. Glassware should be allowed to remain in the cleaning solution for several hours and rinsed with nitric acid prior to washing with water. It is best not to use soap on glassware that is used in experiments, because any soap not completely removed will tend to hold activity on the glass.

The decontaminating agent to be used will often depend upon the type of material that needs to be cleaned. In general, wooden objects or surfaces should be removed and buried rather than decontaminated, because any agent used will soak into the wood and cause the activity to penetrate. Other types of porous materials should be treated in the same manner. Special care should be exercised in decontaminating one's hands in order not to break the skin or to render the contaminant in a form that would permit penetration.

Another point that should be considered when decontaminating is the possible damage to equipment when certain agents are used. Thus, although strong acids will effectively clean metal surfaces, the acids will also corrode most metals used in the laboratory, thereby increasing the cost of operation. The damage that may be done should always be balanced against the necessity for rapid decontamination. In the average tracer laboratory,[3] the amounts of materials handled may seldom require drastic decontamination means.

The university that intends to have a course in which radioisotopes are used, or the laboratory that has an active [3] laboratory, should consider that all equipment purchased for this work must remain within the confines of the active laboratory. Decontamination of equipment may be effected to such a degree that the residual activity left will not cause trouble in the next experiment, providing the same equipment is used with the same radioisotope. If equipment is allowed to leave the laboratory for use elsewhere even though it is *clean*, it will not be long before some highly contaminated piece of equipment will be "accidentally" found outside the active laboratory thus acting as a hazard to all concerned. It is desirable, therefore, that one responsible person should be in complete charge of the active laboratory and that the access to this room be made as difficult as possible in order to prevent contamination of a much wider area.

Health Hazards. Radioactivity cannot be seen, heard, or felt. Solutions of radioactive materials look exactly the same as those that contain no activity. Except under

---

[3] An active or tracer laboratory may be defined as one handling one microcurie to three millicurie amounts of radiosubstances.

special circumstances radioactive solids appear to be the same as their "dead" brothers. Although the radiations are not perceptible to the five senses, they are exceedingly dangerous unless properly controlled. The hazards of working with radioactivity are not encountered in other laboratories. However, the hazards found in all laboratories, such as ingestion, inhalation, and accidents involving injuries, become more acute in the radiochemical laboratory because of the danger of absorbing radioactive materials as well as chemically poisonous substances. Superimposed on all the usual laboratory hazards is the constant bombardment of uncontrolled radiation. However, as K. Z. Morgan has so aptly said, "Radiation need not be feared, but it must be respected." Therefore, in order to protect himself, the student should enter the field of radioactive tracers with an understanding of what is taking place. Provided he follows a few simple rules regarding the use and handling of radioactive materials, he should have no reason to fear the consequences.

A hazardous condition in relation to the health of the laboratory personnel may be defined as any radioactivity which, because of its position, may be a source of radiation above maximum permissible, or because of its location may be easily inhaled, ingested, or unknowingly transported elsewhere by the members of the laboratory. As has been discussed before, thorough periodic surveys will detect any contamination that may be a hazard. Yet, it is important to point out that anyone who is making such a survey must consider the impossible as being the possible. One must investigate all cracks, corners, and other hard to get at places for possible activity. Dusts that collect in the upper parts of laboratory hoods are excellent absorbers, and activity will often be found in this material.

One of the most important operations in the laboratory

using radioactive materials is housekeeping. If the student has not learned that the laboratory must be kept clean in order to do precise work, he must learn this before using radioactive materials. The importance of cleanliness cannot be stressed too much, because not only are experimental results affected, but the health of the individual is at stake as well. Only too often have the authors seen laboratories where dust has collected on unused reagent bottles, behind reagent bottles on the shelves, in cracks between sinks and laboratory benches, and particularly in and around hoods. Even when the laboratory can financially support a technician whose duties are to keep the laboratory in spotless condition, the dusts are often found. It is not that the laboratory supervision has been lax in general housekeeping but that the importance of absolute spotlessness has never been fully impressed upon the personnel using the laboratory. As soon as one begins to use radioactive materials and assiduously tries to follow all the activity, only then does he realize that there is a great deal more to keeping a laboratory clean than what normally meets the eye.

It may appear that the subject of dust in the laboratory is being over-treated. This is not so. No matter how much is written on the subject, not enough will have been said. Through the agency of dust, radioactivity can and will enter the body. The greatest damage possible for a certain amount of radioactive substance can be done when it becomes fixed inside the body. We are speaking here of uncontrolled radiation since the radioactive tracers as used in medicine and biology are prescribed in controlled doses and are given to the patient only under strict regulations and supervision. Dust carrying activity which enters the body through the nasal passages enters the lungs and then, at close range and in soft, easily damaged tissue, it begins to destroy the body cells. The possibility of absorption of radioactive materials by the blood in the lungs cannot be overlooked, because this action will allow the activity to be transported to and deposited in other parts of the body. A considerable fraction of the inhaled radioactive material is held up temporarily in the upper respiratory tract where it is swallowed permitting entry into the body by way of the digestive tract.

We have discussed at length dust and its passage into the body. Since dust is an excellent carrier for radioactivity, we must also consider its transportation into other parts of the building of which the active laboratory is usually only a small portion. Here we must realize that dust may be carried on clothing, or that the shoes worn in the active laboratory may become contaminated due to walking in a spill on the floor. The clothes may become contaminated due to contact with the hands. Since activity may be easily transported over wide areas, some provision must be made for leaving all activity in the laboratory. This subject will be considered in detail later.

Inhalation of activity is only one way of getting activity into the body. Another serious method is by ingestion— that is, through the mouth. Sufficient space is not available to outline all possible means of ingesting activity, but the most important modes will be described and the student may consider others for himself.

Consider the methods used in eating. Fingers as well as knives, forks, and spoons are used. Just as long as utensils are used for transporting food to the mouth there is little opportunity for whatever may be on the hands to enter the digestive system. The act of eating using utensils may be compared to the chemist using tongs, tweezers, and other tools to handle activity in order not to contaminate his hands. Thus, the first thing that must be remembered is that activity must not get on the hands. This point again cannot be overstressed, because unwittingly one will pass his hand over his face, rub his ear or eye, scratch his head, or blow his nose. All these acts bring the hand close to the mouth and provide the opportunity for activity to enter the body. Sandwiches, candy, and similar foods are usually held in the hand while eating. If the hands are contaminated there will be direct passage of activity into the body. Smoking either a pipe or particularly a cigarette is an excellent means of ingesting radioactivity.

Too often, the student of chemistry will fill a pipette using his mouth to provide suction. Needless to say this cannot be tolerated at any time in a laboratory using radioactive materials. The laboratory must be equipped with syringes which provide for remote control as well as protection from ingestion. It should be noted that anything that is contaminated or used in an active laboratory should never be placed in or near the mouth. In this respect one important rule should be mentioned at this point. Eating, drinking, and smoking in the active laboratories are not permitted. By this time, it is sincerely hoped that the student is cognizant of the hazards which surround the use of his hands in the laboratory. He should never touch the phone or a drinking fountain with contaminated hands. The notebooks and pencils used in the tracer laboratory should never leave it. He must remember that wherever he puts his hands there is a possibility that that place may be active or that he may contaminate the spot. In either case the hands will carry activity which may then be ingested without difficulty and without the knowledge of the individual until it is too late. Again let it be said that the *safe* use of radioactive materials is no more dangerous than handling the normal stock of chemicals.

All activities in which glass equipment is used carry with them the hazard of broken glass. Glass that is chipped or broken must be discarded at once. Special pieces of equipment that are difficult or expensive to fabricate may be repaired, but only after a very thorough job of decontamination has been done. Even then the repair should be attempted only by a person who is entirely conversant with the hazards involved and has a knowledge of how the equipment has been used. Broken glass usually results in an injury. These injuries are too often not properly cared for in the average student laboratory. However, in a radiochemical laboratory special precautions must be exercised. Immediately following the injury, the wound should be thoroughly washed by cleansing in a stream of tap water for at least five minutes. Then the injured must report immediately to the person in charge of the laboratory and to a competent physician. On reporting to the physician the injured should be able to explain what has occurred and what radioisotope has been used. No person should be allowed to work with radioactive materials who has an open wound, particularly on his hands.

If radioactive substances have been ingested accidentally, competent medical advice must be secured immediately. The physician should know the amount and type of activity that has been ingested. It should be noted that the toxicity of radioactive substances (except for certain transuranics) is not due to the element but rather to the activity. However, the toxicity depends upon the type of radiation, the half-life of the isotope, the tissue in which the element tends to deposit, the mode of metabolism in the body, and the rate of elimination from the body. The most toxic appear to be the alpha emitting isotopes of intermediate half-life generally in the order of 10^5 years. Some of the long-lived beta emitters that are deposited in the bone, such as strontium-90, are especially hazardous.

Direct radiation of the body by beta and gamma rays

is a hazard that must be controlled. The pioneer workers did not clearly realize the dangers inherent in the experiments they were performing. During a demonstration or a lecture it was accepted that the lecturer would illustrate his experiments by placing his hand in the path of extremely hard gamma radiations in order to obtain the shadow of the bones. In this manner these men received excessive dosages.[4] Today it is not necessary to repeat these experiments. Therefore, the operator using radioactive materials should provide himself with adequate shielding.

Alpha and soft beta radiation will not penetrate the outer layers of the skin. However, this fact does not license the scientist to use his hands in direct contact with any vessel containing radioactive substances. Since beta rays have rather discrete ranges, the distance that a person maintains between any part of his body and the source of activity becomes the important factor.

Gamma radiation, due to its penetrating qualities, cannot be considered in the same manner as alpha or beta radiations. By assuming that the inverse square law holds for volumes larger than point sources, as one approaches the source a rough but practical calculation can be made regarding the closest distance from a source at which it is "safe" to work. This distance will depend, of course, upon the size of the source, the energy of the rays, and the amount of activity involved. It can readily be determined that, where gross activities are present, experimentation is out of the question unless heavy shields are maintained between the operator and the equipment.

External radiation due to alpha sources may be generally disregarded since the alpha radiation has such a low penetration in the skin. In fact, the range of alpha particles in air is of the order of only a few centimeters for the most

[4] The amount of radiation received.

energetic rays. The greatest health hazards involved when alpha emitters are used are ingestion and inhalation and skin penetration.

Levels of Radiation. The hazards as mentioned above depend upon the amount and kinds of activity involved. Not only health hazards but also the kind of experiments are dependent upon the amount of active material that is available or for which there is adequate protection.

Several articles have been written about the amount of radioactive materials that are considered safe in tracer, intermediate, and high-level laboratories. Each one of these levels presents its own series of problems. In general, the high or curie level will be found only in radio-isotope production or in medical therapy laboratories. In these laboratories protection and operation become quite complex. The intermediate level laboratory (five to one thousand millicuries of beta and one to five hundred millicuries of gamma emitters) are usually production, medical therapy, or biological experimentation laboratories. The tracer or microcurie level is found in the control, student, tracer experiment, and production laboratories.

Since this book is primarily for the beginner, only the tracer level laboratories, both beta and beta-gamma, will be considered in detail. In these laboratories the radiation levels or the degree of hazard may be broken down into three sections. The first of these is the counting room level, wherein less than five microcuries of gamma and 0.10 microcuries of beta radiation are used. In general, protection from these sources can be had by providing sufficient distance and enforcing proper handling procedures. The second level of radiation encountered in the tracer laboratory will be in the investigation in progress. At this point the level of active materials may be one hundred microcuries of beta or as high as one millicurie of gamma activity.

The highest level of radiation will be centered about the receiving and standardization of the original material that is purchased. The hazard involved will depend upon the amount and type of material that has been obtained from the supplier.

The receiving of the active shipment and preparation of the standard should be delegated to a competent person who fully understands the hazards involved and knows how to handle amounts of activity above tracer levels. The essential reason for the laboratory is investigations using radioactive materials. Here, then, is the point at which the greatest hazard exists, because undoubtedly there will be several persons in the same small area using tracer levels of activity. Each person who has an experiment in progress represents a potential hazard to himself and all others in the same laboratory. For this reason the total amount of activity incorporated into an individual experiment must be kept as low as possible and yet be sufficient to permit accurate results. It is important that the standards or supplies be kept in properly shielded containers and in designated locations, preferably in a locked receptacle.

Detection of Health Hazards. Several instruments used for laboratory contamination surveys have been mentioned. These instruments can also be used to detect any dangerous levels of radiation that may be present around an experiment. These survey instruments, although they are necessary to the proper operation of the laboratory, are valuable only for indicating contaminated areas or for indicating the level of activity in an experiment at the moment the reading is taken and at the particular location of the sensitive portion of the detector. These instruments usually give an indication of the rates of radiation in milliroentgens per hour. This information is valuable in that it may be used to calculate the average time the operator may stay in that area. However, these instruments do not indicate the amount of radiation that has been received by the operator in the course of any period of time in the laboratory.

A recording, or at least an indicating, type of ionization chamber located at some strategic spot in the laboratory that will indicate momentary readings over an eight-hour period, or record the total integrated radiation received during any specified period, is extremely useful in any tracer laboratory and is an absolute must whenever the amounts of active materials, particularly gamma emitters, are greater than five millicuries.

One method of indicating the amount of activity present in the laboratory air is to collect on paper or metal foil the active particles by precipitating them from a stream of air with an electrical discharge. The paper or foil is then inserted in a counting chamber and checked for total activity. Knowing the efficiency of the counter, the volume of air that has passed through the instrument, and the time of collection, the total amount of activity in the laboratory air can be calculated. Actually this method indicates only the relative amount present in the laboratory during the test, but this information is often valuable since this activity will be indicated as natural background or may not be detected in any other manner. It should be noted that there is in the air at all times a certain amount of radioactivity from natural sources.

All the instruments mentioned above may be termed general radiation level indicators. The individual working in the laboratory is interested in how much radiation he receives during any period of time. Also the laboratory supervision is definitely interested in this same item. The operator is interested because he has heard that radiation may result in permanent injury. The supervisor is interested because of his concern for the welfare of the operator and because of the legal aspects involved. In order to protect both parties, the operator is required to wear personal monitoring instruments whenever he is in the laboratory. These instruments are of several types.

The pocket ionization chambers that are charged each day and read at the end of the working period are valuable indicators of the total gamma radiation that has been received by the individual. These instruments have a pencil clip which enables the wearer to place them at any strategic or predetermined location on his clothes. The pocket ionization chambers do not indicate the amount of beta radiation that has been received since the chamber walls are too thick to permit penetration by beta rays of average energy. The pocket type meter may be subject to accidental discharge. For this reason, it is advisable to use them in pairs. However, even when two meters are worn, they may be discharged by a sharp blow, such as they will receive when dropped. Another source of error is discharge due to moisture retained inside the cap, thus allowing the charge to leak across the insulation. In high humidity areas the accuracy of these instruments will be materially reduced. These defects have been minimized in recent pocket ionization chambers, but it should be said that these instruments have much greater value when correlated with some other type of indicator. Another type of personal ionization chamber that may be purchased is the visual pocket chamber. These instruments are similar to electroscopes in that they contain a scale which is traversed by a fiber as the instrument is discharged. The scale can be read through an eyepiece that is an integral part of the instrument. The pocket electroscope will indicate the total radiation (gamma) that has been received in any length of time from charging to discharge.

A third type of indicator and perhaps the most valuable, since a permanent record is obtained, is the film badge. This is essentially a metal clip with a window in one-half of the face. A piece of dental film contained in its paper wrapper is inserted in the badge in such manner that one-half the film is exposed to radiation only through the paper covering of the film and the other half is shielded by the metal of the clip. Thus, one-half of the film may be exposed to beta radiation which can penetrate the paper and the other half is exposed only to the most energetic beta rays and those gamma rays that produce sufficient ionization in the film to cause exposure. One disadvantage of the film badge is that low energy gamma and X-rays produce much more blackening of the unshielded film than the high energy gamma rays. This makes it difficult to distinguish between beta exposure and low energy gamma and X-ray exposure. A major fault that can be found when using film is that the amount of radiation received is not known until after the film has been developed. If the usual procedure is followed the film may not be developed for one or two weeks after the excessive radiation has been received and this may be too late. If film badges and pocket meters are used as a unit and the pocket meters read every day, then when the ionization chambers indicate a high level (this level may be predetermined and should be considerably less than the daily tolerance dose) the film should be developed and read. In this manner the time lag after excessive radiation has been received will be materially reduced. However, the best method is to have periodic monitoring of the working area or use a visual type ionization chamber and require that the operator leave the active area after a certain amount of radiation has been recorded or calculated to have been taken. This level should be somewhat lower than the daily permissible dose and may reasonably be set at fifty milliroentgens. However, to offset the disadvantages is the fact that the film will record conveniently more radiation than can be detected by any other means commercially available at the present time. Also, as has been mentioned, the film becomes a permanent record of the exposure to radiation by the individual.

Film detectors may be made up in a variety of forms. A small piece of film can be enclosed in a ring, thus allowing the worker to obtain information on how much more radiation his hands receive than other parts of his body. Small film holders can be obtained and the films posted wherever a record of the radiation intensity may be desired.

Although the detection instruments that are on the market today may have certain disadvantages under specific conditions, they are the most practical that have been devised to give as much vital information as possible. It will remain for future electronic engineers, physicists, and chemists to build more delicate and sturdy equipment that will enable the scientist to measure and record more accurately the entire range of radiations that are harmful to man in order that the individual who works with the more dangerous of these radiations will know how much excess radiation he has received daily. Undoubtedly some of these future instruments are being drafted today. The development of these instruments to practical perfection will be a boon to all who use X-rays and radioisotopes.

Before leaving the subject of health hazards, it would not be out of place to discuss what intensity of radiation may be considered dangerous. The International Congress has set up its standards and the American Medical Association has its standards which are more stringent. It is well known that the "Manhattan District" set a "tolerance" of one hundred milliroentgens per day as the limit for its personnel. There has been some question in the light of knowledge gained through the large-scale production of radioactive materials that even this limit may be too high. At the present time no organization has come forward to state that the "tolerance" levels must be lowered. Actually it is not known for certain just what the tolerance should be. One statement that can be made is that every individual who uses or prepares radioactive substances must keep his total dose as close to zero as is possible. Not only must the total radiation received over a period of time be kept to a minimum, but also the rate at which this radiation is received must be kept at a low level. There is evidence that has been described by many biologists, biochemists, and radiologists that the rate of irradiation is highly important. It is known that the body recovers slowly from low level, low rate of irradiation but that high intensity radiation over a short period of time will cause greater damage than when the same dose of radiation is received over a longer period of exposure. It is evident that whoever uses radioactive substances must ever be alert to dangerous levels of radiation, to total radiation received, to the rate in roentgens per hour received, and to use common sense in all his experiments.

Natural Hazards. This chapter cannot be logically concluded without mentioning the normal radiation that everyone everywhere receives each day. This information has not been publicized to the extent that it should be. This radiation comes to all in the form of cosmic rays and the secondary processes derived from them as well as from natural sources in the earth. Radium, although it is a rare element in large enough quantities to be commercially economical to recover, and uranium are present in most rocks in minute quantities. Radon, being a gas, escapes from the surface of the rock. Once this activity is in the air, the decay products may easily remain in the air by becoming absorbed on dust particles and thus give rise to a more or less constant value of activity in the air we breathe. Cosmic radiation is constantly bombarding us. Whenever the particles that make up cosmic radiation achieve a direct hit on an atom, there is undoubtedly some radioactive substance produced. Cosmic radiation certainly ionizes the air or other matter which it penetrates and this ionization, though small, has its effect. Recently it has been shown that the nitrogen of the air when bombarded by cosmic radiation produces carbon-14, a radioisotope with weak beta emission (0.15MEV) and of long half-life (5,700 years). Although carbon-14 is considered dangerous in many respects and the total amount of carbon-14 in the atmosphere is tremendous, the actual quantity available to the individual through inhalation is exceedingly small. Nevertheless, this activity forms a part of the natural radiation everyone receives daily.

In addition, most people have had X-rays for one reason or another. The total "dose" received during the exposure of one film to obtain a picture of the chest is often far more than the careful scientist will receive in a month working with greater than tracer levels. Another apparently innocuous way of receiving extraneous and uncalled for X-radiation is from the small X-ray machines seen in many shoe stores. These machines are supposedly used to view the manner in which the foot spreads in a shoe. However, one must remember that these rays are adding to the total radiation dosage received even though they are considered "safe."

Summing up the hazards that are involved whenever radioactive materials are used, it may be said that those who plan to incorporate active materials in experiments must learn to be critical of each and every move that is made throughout the experiment. He must become sensitive to poor housekeeping in the laboratory and must constantly be aware of the possible sources of contamination and radiation beams that would cause unhealthy overexposures either externally or internally. Then, again, it can be repeated that radiation need not be feared but must be respected.

CHAPTER II

OPERATION OF A RADIOLABORATORY

OPERATION OF A RADIOLABORATORY

Personnel. The safe and efficient operation of a radio-laboratory depends entirely upon the personnel. Those who are to use radioisotopes must be chosen with extreme care. A careless person will endanger the whole laboratory and he may contaminate the laboratory, thus making it useless for continued radiochemical work. This statement applies not only to the active laboratory but to all laboratories or rooms in which radioactivity is used or stored. The amount of radioactivity that could cause erroneous results is very small indeed.

The attitude of each applicant toward radioactivity must be evaluated prior to allowing him the use of the laboratory. Certainly in the university the students who are accepted for the laboratory course would have shown by their previous laboratory work any attitudes that would not be permissible in the active laboratory. In the research center, the interviewer must not be misled by the fact that the applicant has had a course in tracer chemistry.

Not only must the tracer chemist have the proper attitude, but also he must be completely willing to work with radioactive substances. He must feel that less than adequate safety precautions are being enforced in the laboratory. As soon as the radioactivity worker loses these feelings he becomes unsafe in the laboratory and is apt to relax his own precautions and unwittingly overexpose himself and others.

Personnel employed in an active laboratory cannot be too carefully chosen. In the university, the student who desires to learn the techniques used in tracer work must be thoroughly indoctrinated with sound basic principles of self-preservation, self-protection, and a knowledge of safety within the laboratory. The university that has an accredited course in radioactive techniques must certainly desire to recommend its men, but in order to do this the university must first evaluate exceedingly critically the course, the student, and the future results. The university must, in effect, have a "crystal ball" for each student of radioactivity and be able to see this student in another laboratory where he must appear to be the best and the safest worker. Therefore, it behooves those in charge of designing and teaching the course to be overcautious in choosing those who are to reap the rewards.

Supervision. If the responsibility involved in insuring that the radiolaboratory has only the most careful workers appears to be overly great, then the responsibility of choosing a supervisor is even more so. The supervisor is responsible for the safety of all those in the laboratory regardless of the abilities of the individual. On him falls the duty of insuring safety for all who are to use the laboratory. The supervisor must be continually on guard for small differences in the attitude of the operator. The supervisor must satisfy himself and all others in the laboratory that all who are working there know and abide by the rules of the laboratory. He must be trained in the art of the proper use of radioactivity in order that he may be able to detect the improper use of these materials. The many little differences between active and cold laboratories must be pointed out by the supervisor and he must constantly be aware of the possibility that the easier way to do the job may be the more dangerous.

All the activity that is used or stored in the laboratory is the responsibility of the supervisor. He must insure that complete records are kept as to who received activity and the amount. Not only who has the active material but also what was done with the waste solutions must be the responsibility of the supervisor. In larger laboratories this responsibility and authority may be delegated to one person who will keep accurate and complete records of all radioactive materials.

Supervision of an active laboratory entails constant alertness to the possibility that one or two in the laboratory are doing all the work. This can be readily checked, since the film badges may often indicate who is receiving the most radiation. Some careful consideration must be given to this situation, because the worker with consistently high film badge readings may be a careless worker. Also, it may be that certain operations are not properly protected. In any case each overexposure must be thoroughly investigated by the supervisor. If possible the cause should be located. If the worker is at fault and is consistently so, it may be in order to transfer this worker to less hazardous work. Whatever the result of the investigation some positive action must be taken.

Usually some state or federal agency must approve the location and the safety of an installation. This approval does not guarantee the safety of the installation. Too many times the training of the supervision is inadequate to cope with many of the problems that arise during the operation of the laboratory. Also, there is the possibility that the laboratory personnel are well trained but "polish up" the laboratory when an inspection is due so that the inspector does not see the day-to-day conditions. If the active material has been received from the Atomic Energy Commission their representatives will make periodic inspections.

They can, oftentimes, give on-the-spot advice to those who desire to maintain high standards, or they will be able to obtain what information may be needed for the proper operation of the laboratory. However, these inspections are again usually "prepared for" by the laboratory, since there is usually advance notice of the inspection. Regardless of the various inspections that are made, the supervisor of the laboratory is responsible for the conditions. Therefore, he should require that high standards be maintained at all times.

Procurement. Radioactive materials may be obtained from several sources, depending upon what kind of radioactivity is wanted. Radioisotopes in quantities may be obtained from the Oak Ridge National Laboratories after the necessary requests and approvals have been made by the Isotopes Branch of the Atomic Energy Commission at Oak Ridge, Tenn. However, this is not the only source of active materials. The United States Bureau of Standards has for sale a limited number of standards which are useful as references. Radium, polonium, and some of the decay products of uranium may be obtained from various mining companies in Canada. Radioisotopes may be obtained from the several types of accelerators. The most notable of these producers are the cyclotrons, Van de Graaf machines, and the betatrons.

Although the average tracer laboratory will not normally ship radioactive materials, it is essential that some knowledge of the Interstate Commerce Commission's regulations regarding shipment of these materials should be had by the supervision of the laboratory. The full text of these regulations may be found in the "Federal Register," Vol. 12, No. 220, pp. 7329-7333. These regulations give explicit directions in regard to packaging and shipping of radioactive materials.

Under these regulations, radioactive materials are divided into three groups. Group I consists of radioactive materials emitting gamma rays only or gamma rays and alpha and/or beta rays. Group II are radioactive materials that emit neutrons only or neutrons and alpha, beta and/or gamma rays. Group III materials are those which emit only alpha or beta rays. Packaging of these materials is given in detail. The most important factors in packaging radioactive materials are shielding in order to protect those who must handle the package as well as those who may be nearby; shielding in order to prevent damage to sensitive materials such as unexposed films; and construction of the package in order to prevent leakage in case of accidents. Regulations covering these points are very explicit. Radioactive materials are shipped under regulations pertaining to explosives, as Class D poisons, and must be labeled as such. These labels carry a certification of the contents of the package and that the package is within the radiation tolerances allowed. There are several exceptions to the marking, labeling, and packaging requirements. The student or the prospective shipper should obtain a copy of the regulations if more detailed information is desired.

Radiation Laboratory Rules. All laboratories have certain rules that are more or less rigidly enforced. Laxness in enforcement of the radiolaboratory rules must not be permitted. These rules are designed for the health and safety of not only those in the laboratory but also for those with whom the laboratory's members may live. It is desirable to have as few rules as possible in order that these will be consistently followed. At the same time the number of rules should be sufficient to embrace all possible activity and protection of the laboratory and its personnel. In the following paragraphs general rules applying to radioactive work will be considered.

1. The permissible level for total or limited body exposure is 0.1 rem.[1] No person should knowingly expose himself or others to greater than this quantity in a twenty-four hour period.

2. The air tolerance is considered to be about 10^{-7} microcuries per cubic centimeter. When the counting rate of the collected sample exceeds this value, the area must be evacuated. If the counting rate of a collected sample exceeds 0.1 of this value, masks must be worn in the area and only emergency work continued.

3. Surface contamination tolerances will vary with the surface being considered. The following tolerances should be considered as maximums permissible at any time, but under no circumstances should they be considered as allowable continuous working conditions.

Item	Instrument	Level [2]
a. Hands	Eck & Krebs counter	350 counts per min.
b. Clothing, table tops, body, etc.	Eck & Krebs counter	250 counts per min.
c. Smear test on tables, floors, equipment	End window G-M counter (smear 12 sq. in. of surface with 2 sq. in. of filter paper)	100 counts per min. of Beta and Gamma
d. Isotope shipping container before returning	Electroscope	Less than 10 mr/24 hr. at surface of package
e. Container smear test	Smear test counted on end window of G-M counter	Less than 100 counts per min.
f. Shoe (inside)	Probe	500 counts per min.

[1] The *rem* stands for roentgen equivalent man and is the quantity of radiation which, when absorbed by man, produces the effect equivalent to the absorption by man of one roentgen of X or gamma radiation.

[2] The counting levels correspond to those obtained with a Geiger-Mueller counter in which one milliroentgen per hour of one Mev gamma radiation at the counter produced about 3000 counts per minute.

Item	Instrument	Level [2]
g. Thyroid	G-M probe counter	400 counts per min. with counter against throat
h. General working areas	Electroscope or ionization chamber instruments	All areas greater than 6 mr/hr. must be roped off and posted.

4. Anyone entering the laboratory must wear personal monitoring meters.

5. Suitable protective clothing must be provided for all visitors and personnel.

6. Rubber gloves, preferably the surgical type, should be worn whenever hand contamination is probable.

7. Combat masks, suitable respirators, or air line hoods should be worn in any area where the airborne concentration of beta and gamma emitters may be greater than 10^{-8} counts per cubic centimeter.

8. Eating, storing, or the preparation of food in any area in which activity is stored or used is forbidden.

9. Smoking in active areas is forbidden.

10. Whenever the possibility of contamination of the person or clothing is present, the individual should (a) keep the fingernails cut short; (b) wash hands thoroughly before eating, drinking, or smoking; (c) refrain from smoking; (d) wash rubber gloves before removing; and (e) utilize available counting facilities as frequently as necessary to determine contamination.

11. Pipetting of active solutions by mouth is forbidden. Glass blowing in laboratories containing active materials should not be permitted.

12. Any person who knowingly swallows, inhales, or receives an injection of radioactive material or who has been overexposed must report to the supervisor and then to a competent physician immediately.

13. All spills must be cleaned and decontaminated to permissible levels immediately.

14. Storage of all activities must be such that observed radiation levels outside the shield are at a minimum, preferably less than 6 mr/hr. Alpha emitters should be stored in a specially constructed container and kept in a well-ventilated hood.

15. Complete records of receipts, transfers, and disposal of radioactive materials must be kept.

16. Disposal of liquid wastes should be such that activity will not deposit in pipes or raise the level of the waste waters above the permissible value (considered to be 10^{-8} microcuries per milliliter).

17. Disposal of solid wastes should be such that no radiation hazard is involved.

Since the laboratory is ultimately responsible for any radiation damage to the personnel, a rather complete medical supervision of the health of those concerned should be set up. This should include a thorough physical examination prior to employment or admittance to the laboratory and periodic blood examinations during the period of employment.

The prior physical examination should include a complete blood analysis. The general health picture of the applicant must be considered particularly in relation to anemia and possible previous overexposure to ionizing radiation. It is essential that the blood be examined by a competent and interested haematologist in order to determine any significant departure from the normal. If this is not done prior to allowing the person entrance to the laboratory for study or work, it will be extremely difficult to interpret any abnormalities that may appear later. Monthly tests of the blood are advisable in order to establish the normal variation of the individual. After the normal variation has been established the periodicity may be extended to quarterly. Certainly the blood should be examined every quarter regardless of the visual health of the worker.

It must be remembered that the blood picture is not a warning but rather a picture of what damage has been done. Any significant changes must be investigated immediately, since changes in the blood picture may indicate a previous overexposure or may indicate an impending illness. In either case the worker should not be allowed to use radioactive materials until a physician indicates that the person may return to the laboratory.

Too often the condition of the hands is overlooked. The physician who undertakes the physical examination should carefully note any and all abnormalities on the hands. He should be particularly careful in regard to the finger tips and the skin around the nails. This is important since, regardless of the caution of the worker, the hands will undoubtedly receive the greatest exposure.

Records. The most important item, other than safety, in the radiolaboratory is complete records. These are important from the viewpoint of knowing the location of active material at all times and how much activity is in the laboratory. Also it is necessary to know who has obtained activity and for what purpose. Only by having records of the various transactions can the supervision be able to report on its disposal, loss by decay, or the extent of the experimental cost per unit of activity received. The records should reveal any losses due to accidents. Control of radioactive materials in the laboratory can be had only with complete records. It is necessary, therefore, that one person be assigned to the receiving, storing, and dispensing of activity. It will be his duty not only to have complete records of material received and used but also the ultimate disposal of these materials. Any activity that is recovered from the experimental work should be listed in a separate record. Examples of these records are shown on pages 43 and 44.

Records of activity are not the only ones that are useful and needed in the active laboratory. Contamination and radiation level records should be kept. Records of hand and shoe or clothing counts are valuable aids to the personnel and particularly the supervisor. Personal exposure records as indicated by the film badges and pocket meters should be kept up to date in order to follow the activity of each individual. Records of the physical examinations and blood smears should be retained by the physician or medical department but should be available to the supervisor at any time.

Each of these records should be kept in such a manner that summaries may be made rapidly and easily. It is advisable to keep a separate activity record for each isotope that is used in the laboratory. Also, any additions to the stock can be indicated by entering the data in red ink. In this manner it becomes simple to determine how much has been received and how much has been used. Any over-tolerance radiation readings might be entered on the proper forms in order to highlight any dangerous levels that can be better protected the next time the experiment is made.

Several useful forms are shown on pages 43 and 44. A handy method for indicating the radiation level and smear test results is to use a line drawing of the laboratory showing the location of the most important objects as hoods, desks, sinks, doors, and windows. The spot where the radiation reading is taken and the direction of the reading as well as the areas used for smearing are numbered on the drawing. At one side these numbers are recorded along with the reading in milliroentgens per hour or counts per minute. Any values that are tolerance or overtolerance may be circled in red. When dated and signed by the surveyor, this sheet will become a permanent record of the condition of the laboratory.

Room Arrangements. It is not the desire of the authors to specify that certain room arrangements are the only ones allowable; however, there are some arrangements that have many advantages. The most practical arrangement can only be obtained when a new building is proposed for the active laboratory or when extensive remodeling is in order. Usually neither of these procedures is possible. Therefore, the arrangement of the active laboratory will depend upon the particular situation and the availability of space. In any case there are several factors that must be considered in the general arrangement of rooms.

Three levels of activity may be considered when setting up an active laboratory. These are counting levels (<0.10 microcuries), radio-assay or tracer levels (<100 microcuries), and process level (>5 millicuries). The levels mentioned above are considered by the authors to be sufficient for the needs of most student laboratories. For those laboratories which intend to process larger amounts of radioactive materials special procedures should be formulated, because the high level laboratory may be handling up to several curies of activity. Since the amount of active material required to produce erroneous results in radio-assay work is very small, it is necessary to maintain the high level laboratory as a separate unit and to allow only one-way traffic of equipment into this laboratory. The opportunity for contamination of clothing, hands, and, of course, equipment is very great in these laboratories. Therefore, any equipment used in this laboratory should remain there. Special laboratory coats should be worn by those who use this room and by those who must periodically enter it. If it is possible, a separate small change-room could be inserted between the high level laboratory and the rest of the active area. Needless to say there should be an emergency exit from this room either directly outside or to a place of safety.

In the simplest case, the high-level laboratory may be combined with the radio-assay laboratory. Under these circumstances the above statements regarding cross contamination constantly must be borne in mind by the personnel. Many student laboratories will certainly be in this class. That is, there will not be sufficient space to provide the number of rooms required for a complete arrangement. Usually these laboratories will not require more than a few millicuries of activity at any particular time, and the necessary preparations of standard solutions can be made during hours in which no other experimentation is in progress.

The counting room should be a separate room at all times in order to maintain extremely low levels of activity. If quantities of activity are present in the counting room, the background of the counters is apt to increase, the counters may become contaminated, or the room may become contaminated. Whichever condition may prevail, the value of the counting room is destroyed particularly if very accurate results are desired. All solid samples entering the counting room should be covered in order to prevent spreading activity, and liquid samples should be contained in two concentric vessels in case of breakage.

A simple way in which the necessary rooms can be combined is shown in Figure 1. The small anteroom can be used as a dressing and shower room. This room should be considered as a must for all active laboratories. This should not be considered as the ultimate in design but rather as a basis for improvement by those who intend to install active laboratories. Each individual will have rather pre-formed ideas in regard to how the active laboratory should be arranged and should be encouraged to develop those ideas. But, before the laboratory is constructed or revised, those in charge should endeavor to determine all possible loopholes where danger of contamination or hazardous conditions may exist. One must be constantly on guard not to locate active laboratories in a manner that may be ideal in so far as those who are in the laboratory

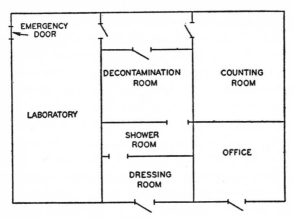

FIG. 1. Room arrangements.

are concerned but far from ideal when surrounding areas to the sides, above, and below are considered. Whenever possible it is desirable to locate the active laboratory such that available natural shielding is utilized.

Auxiliary Equipment. Many small details are involved in setting up an efficient active laboratory. Some of these are almost necessities and the laboratory will be inefficient without them. Others, although they are not required, will serve to improve the operations of the laboratory and will produce the desired effect on those who work in, visit, or inspect the laboratory.

Since film badges and pocket meters are used daily by

those in the laboratory and must be transported elsewhere for processing, a small rack with holes cut in the surface the size and shape of the meters will be desirable. The arrangement should be such that each person's meters are located directly opposite his name. This rack should be located in the anteroom or a checking room, if this is available. It should be placed so that no extraneous radiation will be picked up by the film badges thereby giving erroneous readings caused by radiation received during hours when the laboratory personnel are not present.

Air conditioning in the laboratory and counting rooms is very desirable but not absolutely necessary. Some conditioning can be obtained through the proper use of hoods and air filters in the windows. Air filters of some type are a necessity if dust from outside is to be kept at a minimum. In the average laboratory the hoods operating at an air flow of 100 lineal feet per minute will usually keep the laboratory comfortable. Hood exhausts should be so arranged that air will not be drawn from one hood into the room while another is in operation. However, in the counting rooms where no such ventilation is available a simple air-conditioning unit may be installed. This is desirable for another reason. Although counting equipment has been operated in a normal laboratory with success there are some who believe that counting equipment should be located in well-shielded, air-conditioned rooms. It is reasoned that under ideal conditions of constant temperature and humidity Geiger-Mueller counting equipment will operate more consistently and last longer.

Shower space should be provided for those who are in the laboratory. The showers might be located in the suggested anteroom. Under no circumstances should the showers be at some remote spot since the constant trips to the shower room may leave a trail of radioactivity in the building.

Separate lockers or other means of keeping clothes worn in the laboratory separated from the street clothes should be available. When this is done the laboratory clothes can be worn for longer periods of time provided they are not contaminated over the limit. Clothing that gives a count close to or above the limit should be washed or destroyed. In either case the operation should be supervised by someone who knows the situation.

Some consideration should be given to notebooks and records that are used in the active laboratory. Keeping adequate notes of experimental work creates a problem since it is desirable to record data directly in the notebook. If the notebook is to be retained in the active laboratory, it should be monitored periodically in order to detect any contamination. If the notebooks are to be removed from the active laboratory, then some precautions must be maintained to insure that no activity will be accidentally removed with them. The treatment of notebooks is particularly difficult in student laboratories. This problem may be solved by supplying forms for each experiment on which the student will record his data and, at the end of the laboratory period, he will transfer the data to his notebook. This, of course, should be done at a designated table probably located in the anteroom. The original data sheets may then be filed in a special storage cabinet or disposed of.

Special equipment used in the laboratory for handling of activity will be considered more specifically in the next two chapters. However, since this equipment is specialized, it should be mentioned at this point particularly in regard to the general considerations that should be given before obtaining this equipment. The greater proportion of the pieces that are used can be made from standard laboratory tools. For instance, it is desirable to sheath the tips of tongs with rubber tubing or plastic materials that may be easily removed and destroyed, thus protecting the tongs from contamination and at the same time preventing loss of activity, because a beaker or flask might slip in the steel jaws. Tongs of various lengths should be provided. Also some positive method of gripping is necessary.

Hemostats are valuable adjuncts to use in place of screw clamps particularly when the radiation level is low or when it is necessary to reduce the exposure time. Unless it is requisite for control of flow, the hemostat offers the quickest and surest method of pinching off rubber or plastic tubing.

Small wood cases the width of the sample mounting card with the sides slotted in order to insert the cards are helpful for storing samples that are being retained either for decay studies or for reference.

Waste jars for liquid wastes should be available. Such containers should be properly protected for the usual safety requirements and for radiation. Suitable metal cans must be provided for contaminated paper or equipment in the laboratory. Any wastes that are produced in the laboratory cannot be allowed to leave the laboratory except under proper supervision.

RADIOACTIVE MATERIALS RECORD

Isotope P^{32} Half-life 14.2 days

Location barricade P^{32}

	Alpha ___ Mev
Radiation	Beta 1.68 Mev
	Gamma ___ Mev

Date	Remarks	mc received	mc dispersed	mr/hr. 6 in. over open vessel	Transferred to	For
9/2/48	In Section A-1 by L.B.E.	10				
9/2/48	Removed by W.T.S.—Sec. B-1		1	12	Room 7 Dabney	C.A.B.
9/4/48	Removed by H.A.S.—Sec. B-1		1	12	Room 9 Science	A.D.M.
9/4/48	Removed by K.G.W.—Sec. B-1		5	10	Room 4 Biology	C.L.C.
9/10/48	In Section A-1 by K.Z.M.	10		5		
9/11/48	Removed by J.H.W.		3	12	Room 3 Dabney	W.T.S.

LABORATORY WASTE DISPOSAL DATA

Date	Active Material	Milliliters of Liquid in waste	Solid mr/hr. at 6 in.	Disposal	By
9/6/48	P^{32}	10		Liquid waste jar for decay	G.P.M.
9/10/48	P^{32}	100		Liquid waste jar for decay	E.C.M.
9/10/48	P^{32}		50	Solid waste container	J.W.J.
9/20/48	Liquid wastes	200		Transferred by special truck to waste disposal system	J.H.R.
	Solid wastes		100		

PERSONAL MONITORING RECORD *

Date 9/2/48

Background 10 counts per minute

Name	Right hand	Left hand	Clothing	Shoes	Remarks
B.R.W.	20	20	10	10	
F.J.S.	25	30	20	50	
K.G.W.	50	300	200	75	
V.L.S.	75	100	100	150	
R.T.O.	150	350	100	125	
R.T.O.	20	100			After scrubbing

* This form is for use with an Eck & Krebs or Geiger-Mueller probe. Special counters have been designed which will register both sides of both hands and the shoe soles in one operation.

CONSTRUCTION OF THE RADIOLABORATORY

CONSTRUCTION OF THE RADIOLABORATORY

Introduction. The major difference between the tracer laboratory and the usual chemical laboratory is the health hazard which is related to the radiations that are emitted by the active isotopes. Although the general construction of the individual tracer laboratory may be similar to any other laboratory, the materials of construction, several basic ideas of design, and the use of the laboratory are different in many respects. In this chapter the design and construction will be considered. The use of the tracer laboratory will be the subject of Chapter IV.

It is recognized that many institutions will not be able to build a separate unit for the tracer laboratory even though this is by far the best solution. However, the ultimate goal of those who intend to continue to provide facilities for teaching and research using radioactive materials should be the construction of a building or buildings exclusively designed for this use. The idea of having several buildings is directly connected with cost of installation and the health hazards. If several small buildings are designed for radioactive work, they may be used for different levels of activity. That is, one building could be constructed for the use of high-level experiments or production of radioisotopes, whereas others may be built at less cost since shielding of low level or tracer activities is not as extensive as for high-level work. Also it is extremely

47

difficult to perform tracer-level experiments in a high-level laboratory. Even though it may not be feasible to erect separate buildings, the larger installations will want to have several completely segregated laboratories which may be used for various different activity levels or for entirely unrelated isotopes. The latter case may be the condition in some of the larger hospital laboratories where the chance of cross-contamination may be eliminated by the use of small individual laboratories for different isotopes.

At institutions where only a single course has been contemplated the revision of existing laboratories will undoubtedly be the first consideration. Existing facilities can be used, provided proper precautions have been taken. In many cases the revision of these laboratories may be expensive, but the cost will depend entirely upon the scope of the work to be done. If safe facilities are to be provided, the institution should seriously consider a completely separated building or at least a laboratory as far removed from other laboratories as can be obtained. The reason for this statement will become evident as this chapter is read.

The floor plan of any tracer laboratory will depend upon those who are designing the facility. There seems to be no best plan, and each individual will have his own ideas as to what he considers the best. Therefore, we shall consider only the integral parts of the laboratory and some of the reasons for certain types of arrangements without regard to the number of rooms to be provided. Each facility should contain, as a minimum, a laboratory in which the experiments are conducted, a counting room, a change room or a change-shower room, and an office. The office and change room need not be large and may be combined if the circumstances require it. These units should be so located that one must pass through the change room to enter the active laboratory. It is desirable to maintain the counting room in a location such that active materials are not carried out of the general confines of the laboratory.

After the decision has been made whether to build a new laboratory or to revise existing ones, the materials that are to be used should be examined rather critically. Several materials will be considered in greater detail later. At this time only the general uses of these materials and their relation to the hazards of radioactive materials will be discussed. Regardless of the material desired, it must be remembered that good engineering and construction practices must be followed if a satisfactory laboratory is to be the result. For the outer walls the use of standard design or, if one so desires, special design will be equally good. However, it is possible to incorporate in the outer walls a certain amount of shielding by using special concretes or by providing extra thickness that may be utilized for insulation. The inside walls should be smooth with no sharp corners in which dust or dirt may lodge. The materials used should be such that walls and ceilings can be readily washed without damage. For this purpose transite or other synthetic materials coated with an impervious paint or plastic may be satisfactory. Wherever shielding can be incorporated into the construction this should be done, particularly if it is planned to use gamma emitting materials. Porous materials should be avoided especially at any point where there may be a possibility of a spill. Wood should be used sparingly and then only where it will not be likely to become contaminated. Any substance that is used in the construction should be considered in respect to the ease of decontamination or replacement because of contamination.

Walls. Wall surfaces, as has been just mentioned, should be smooth and constructed of material that can be washed easily. All corners or points where there may be cracks between the furniture and the walls should be sealed in order to prevent active materials getting behind the wall thus producing a hazardous condition. A good acid-resistant, plastic-base type paint that may be sprayed on the walls will be rather effective in any laboratory. Whenever it is possible wall or ceiling fixtures that may be troublesome to keep clean should be eliminated. Installation of moldings except where absolutely necessary for construction should be discouraged. Windows and door frames should be made flush with the wall or sealed into the wall as an integral part of the construction.

Floors. Floors have always been a problem in the active laboratory. Dirt carried in from outside and dust from normal wear may create hazardous conditions. The surface of the floor to be perfect should be nonporous, easy to decontaminate, dustless, resistant to wear, and of course inexpensive. This ideal condition has not been found at present, and several methods are in use which attempt to circumvent one or more of these basic principles. Without further discussion, it may be said that wood floors should be discouraged since they are very easily contaminated to the point where replacement becomes a necessity. Wood, because of its high porosity, cannot be decontaminated. Whenever decontamination has been tried the activity soaks further into the wood. It may appear that some decontamination has been accomplished because the radiation is being absorbed in the wood. What has been said about wood applies equally well to concrete or any other porous material. In order to provide structurally sound floors, wood, metal, or concrete will have to be provided. Of these the concrete appears to offer the best possibilities. Using concrete as a base, the surface may be hardened to give less porosity by one of several methods or another surface that may easily be replaced can be provided. Painting of concrete floors has not proven entirely satisfactory, but it is recommended by many who have had contact with high-level laboratories. Concrete floors are difficult to replace since the contaminated portions must be chipped out and the concrete replaced. This never gives an entirely satisfactory floor after the first replacement. In some tracer-level laboratories concrete floors have been covered with plastic which is sprayed on and can be easily removed by stripping the plastic from the floor. Usually the plastic is protected at points where there will be considerable walking by using rubber mats which may be easily discarded should they become contaminated.

Linoleum blocks or strips set in an asphaltic mastic have been used advantageously in some laboratories to cover the concrete. Wood floors have been covered with linoleum, but the subflooring in this case should be tight; otherwise the linoleum will eventually settle into the crevices and crack. Decontamination is simplified when linoleum tiles are used, since only those squares that are contaminated have to be removed and replacement is not excessively expensive.

Other laboratories have used blotting paper on the floor immediately surrounding the area in which active work is in progress. The blotting paper is then discarded as soon as the work has been completed. Although this method has merit, the continuous walking on the paper will scuff it and produce excessively dusty conditions that are not good.

Desks. Laboratory desks or benches are usually made of wood with several types of working surfaces. The services supplying each position are always in the open and usually in rather awkward locations, particularly for radio-chemical work. A completely new design for the active

laboratory should be developed with the peculiar requirements of the radiochemist in mind. Such a desk would be
fashioned entirely of steel coated with a resistant baked-on
surface. The working surface would consist of stainless
steel with a lip around the sides and front edges and slightly
tilted toward the rear in order to allow the flow of liquid
to a drain at the back. The drain and desk surface would
be one piece. The several services required would be in a
metal case such that, if repairs were necessary, one face
could be removed, but so that normally liquids could not
leak into the case. Valve handles would be placed in an
easily accessible spot so that the chemist would not have
to reach across the desk to turn the valve, thereby risking
an exposure from active materials that may not be too
well shielded. The whole desk should be set up from the
floor in order to facilitate washing underneath, thus allowing no place for contamination or dust to accumulate.

However, since the ideal is not generally available, those
who are planning on a revision of present facilities should
strive to attain as nearly ideal conditions as funds and
supplies will allow. Therefore, we may discuss certain
aspects of the ideal as being the minimum, and those who
are able may provide the more nearly perfect conditions.
It should be remembered that the perfect laboratory is
yet to be designed and, since all laboratories have their
faults, it behooves those who are intending to construct
tracer laboratories to examine critically each portion of
the laboratory with the goal of reducing all chances of
contamination to a minimum.

In every tracer laboratory all working surfaces should
be covered with a stainless steel sheet having a lip on three
sides to prevent active material spilling on the floor. This
sheet should drain to the rear of the desk into a steel
trough. Although stainless steel is not resistant to certain

acids, it does provide the best surface and may be decontaminated rather easily. Some may argue that stainless steel is expensive; however, it would require but very few spills on the ordinary bench surface to more than pay for the stainless. As a further protection, many laboratories use blotting paper over the stainless steel. If a spill occurs the absorbent paper may be discarded leaving the original surface uncontaminated.

Reagent shelves at the back of the laboratory desk should be covered with metal or blotting paper. If blotting paper is used it should be replaced every week in order to reduce the dust hazard in the laboratory. Drawer pulls, door knobs, and valve handles on the service lines should be made for easy decontamination. The first two may be made of plastic or metal and the last made of plastic. Although these parts should not become contaminated, they do, and therefore should be easy to remove for decontamination.

Sinks. Disposal of waste solutions in the chemical laboratory has often posed some complex problems. As has been mentioned earlier the active laboratory wastes only add to the complexity of the problems encountered. The whole sewer system should be checked for places where hazardous conditions could exist. Certainly there should be no possible way for any active wastes to get out of the system and into the water supply. Even though the active material passed into the sewer system may be well below the tolerances allowed, the possibility of active materials precipitating on the sewer lines cannot be overlooked. Another source of active liquids that will go through the sewer system is the decontamination of equipment used in the experiments, since usually this will be done in the sinks.

Stainless steel of welded construction has been found to be very satisfactory. The drainboards and sink should be fashioned so that the least number of welds are made. Whenever it is possible, all corners should be curved rather than square because less difficulty will be encountered in keeping the sink clean. The traps should be a continuous flow type but made in such a manner that they may be easily cleaned. Also they should be arranged so that any broken glass or bottle caps that may be contaminated cannot get further into the sewer system.

The drying boards may be made of either aluminum or stainless steel. The bottom edge of this board should drain into the sink and may be made a part of the sink. If this is done, one can be assured that any activity will be washed into the waste system. Instead of the usual pegs for hanging glassware, some laboratories have used another system rather successfully. The beakers and small equipment are placed on large wire mesh of varying sizes under which there is a metal trough with a drain directly to the sink. This system prevents drops splashing as they hit the drainboard or sink thus spattering activity. Volumetric flasks can be inverted and the necks set through the wire mesh thus ensuring complete draining and drying. Cylinders are inverted and inserted between pairs of rods with the bases resting on the rods. Many other possibilities will be suggested by those who wish to obtain maximum efficiency with a minimum of contamination. These ideas should be encouraged; however, one must not overdo the design else it will become unsightly, cumbersome, and probably not even used by those who are in the laboratory.

Hoods. The hoods in a radiochemical laboratory are highly important. If they are not properly ventilated or constructed, they become a serious source of danger and contamination. The ventilation of the hood will be considered later when the whole ventilation system is discussed.

Stainless steel is perhaps the best construction material

for the laboratory hood. Even though some acid gases may corrode this material, it will be found to be the easiest to keep clean and to decontaminate. If other materials are considered for the upper parts of the hood, the working surface should be of stainless steel and follow a design similar to other working surfaces. Here again, blotting or absorbent paper should be used to catch any material that may be spilled. The upper parts of the hood may be constructed of any one of the synthetic rock boards coated with an impermeable plastic. These synthetic rock boards are available commercially in several types, some of which are highly nonporous. Aluminum sheet may be considered as a possibility for the hood, particularly if the gases that may pass through it will not attack the metal. Wood or porous materials should not be considered as satisfactory construction materials. Some may doubt the possibility of constructing a satisfactory hood. Although the best construction material has not been developed, the materials mentioned above, except for wood, can be fashioned into hoods that may be maintained in a satisfactory condition if certain additions to be discussed in the next paragraphs are installed. The particular material that is used will, of course, depend upon the funds available and the ability or ingenuity of the designer to make the most out of the materials at hand.

Regardless of the construction of the hood, some method should be provided for washing down the flues and sides. This can be done by installing a spray line in the flues and setting the flues at such an angle that the wash water or acid will drain through the hood into the sewer system. A second set of sprays should be installed near the top of the hood to ensure complete washing of the hood walls particularly behind the baffles. As has been mentioned in another section, the floor of the hood should slope toward the rear in order to drain all liquids into the waste disposal system. If the hoods have been properly designed and fabricated, several kinds of decontaminating agents may be used.

When considering the services to the hood there appear to be two possibilities. In the first case all the valves and connections can be located outside the hood or, in the second case, the valves can be outside with the connections inside. Either one has certain advantages and it will depend upon the local conditions or the type of work that is to be performed which method has the greater number of advantages. In the average tracer laboratory, the second method may be the more logical since all connections can be made inside the hood and the window closed before any operations are carried out, thus eliminating a source of air contamination. At the same time, the valve handles should not become contaminated with this system. However, the chemist must always be alert when making connections inside the hood, because contamination may exist and may be easily transferred to the valve handles outside the hood.

The last important part of the hood is the ventilation. The hood and baffles should be constructed so that the air sweep does not produce any eddy currents. The baffles may be installed so that they may be regulated, thus producing a desired air flow across the face of the hood when the window is in any position. The air flow should be a minimum of one hundred lineal feet per minute when the window of the hood is wide open. If more than one hood is provided the air flow should be the same for all hoods as for a single hood. The total air flow in the ventilating system should be based on the maximum number of hoods that are expected to be open at any one time. If adjustable baffles are used in the hood the air flow rate can be kept more nearly constant through a partially open hood, thus providing capacity for other hoods without taxing the entire system. Before discussing the rest of the ventilating system, it should be mentioned that the hoods should be constructed so that no cracks are left for stray air streams to enter or leave in order to prevent contaminations of the laboratory air.

Ventilation. In the best ventilation system all air brought into the laboratory will be filtered to remove dust and will be removed from the laboratory through the hoods. It is important that the air removed from the active laboratory be filtered in order to prevent spreading active particles outside. With this in mind those who are designing new facilities will be able to provide the best method. For those who are remodeling existing facilities, the problem of proper ventilation becomes serious enough that it should be presented to experts who can advise on the proper procedure. In any case the system should be separated from any other system already in the building because if any breakdown of the equipment occurs the whole building may become highly contaminated. Filtered air may be obtained by using filters that can be purchased on the market and installed in windows.

The flues and ducts used in the ventilating system may be fabricated from the usual materials. Transite and similar materials should not be entirely overlooked, since this type of material has been found to be satisfactory in many ways. If this material is coated or painted on the inside it becomes a very resistant duct. It may be the cheapest and best material when the original cost of installation, ease of decontamination, cost of replacing, and serviceable life are considered. Any painting that is done either in the hoods or ventilating system must be strictly according to the paint manufacturers specifications in order to be completely satisfactory. The plastic-base type or certain acid-resistant paints should be used in order to provide the best chemical resistance.

Contamination of the general area outside the laboratory building must be considered when designing the ventilation system. The extent of the possible contamination will depend upon the kind and amount of active substances that are to be used in the laboratory. The best recommendation that can be made on this subject is that those who are interested in having the safest possible area should consult with both ventilation and health-physics experts who are trained in this subject. The health-physics group is extremely important, since it has become their business to detect all possible situations that may produce hazardous conditions in relation to the health of not only those directly concerned with the use of radioactivity, but also those who may be accidentally exposed to radiation. The size of the laboratory and its work will determine how extensive the ventilation system should be. Here again it can be mentioned that at any particular installation, whether large or small, certain limitations should be placed on the activity involved and that these limits must be rigidly enforced.

Shielding. The kind or type of shielding is perhaps the major difference between the beta and the beta-gamma laboratories. Very light or no shielding other than distance may be possible in the beta laboratory. The light shielding may be glass, plastic, or water. The important factor is that beta radiation is completely stopped in rather thin layers of material depending, of course, upon the density of the material and the energy of the beta rays. However, certain more dense substances such as lead often give rise to X-rays when used to shield the stronger beta radiations such as those from Rh^{106}. This condition should therefore be included when the design of shielding is considered for pure beta emitters.

There are two schools of thought regarding the method of shielding equipment. One group desires area shielding and the other suggests that individual equipment pieces be shielded. Both ideas have their merits and demerits. When area shielding is to be considered one must realize that the shielding will be almost permanent, massive, expensive, and sometimes wasteful in space. All these points must be considered before permanent shielding is erected. In the average student laboratory where a series of experiments involving beta and beta-gamma sources are to be performed, area shielding may tie-up much needed space. Under conditions where unit processes involving high-energy, high-level gamma radiation that are in continuous operation, area shielding may be used to some advantage. However, this suggests much more permanency than would be true in the student laboratory. Equipment shielding, although it may not be as simple to design and construct, will usually be found to save considerable space. Here again, there must be some balance attained between what is available for the laboratory, the type of work to be done, and the cost of installation. Since the average student laboratory will not have sufficient space to erect large permanent barricades in which only a few experiments can be performed, temporary or semi-permanent shields can be erected. Temporary shields may be classified according to the above two theories. That is, a single laboratory bench may be used on which a temporary shield may be erected or each student may set up his own shield immediately around his equipment. For the greater portion of a laboratory course in radioactive techniques, temporary shielding will probably be the best because the shields may be readily stored when not needed and no space is lost due to heavy permanent shields.

In the average tracer laboratory using only beta active

substances, the kind and amount of shielding can be held to a minimum. Except for a few of the most energetic activities and the operations involved in handling or diluting the material as received, the glassware will be sufficient shielding. However, the equipment should never be grasped in the bare hand whenever activity is present. Shielding for larger amounts of beta radioactive elements may range from various thicknesses of plastic to the heavier and more dense metals. In the latter case, there will be the problem of bremsstrahlung caused by the bombardment of the metal with beta rays. Perhaps the best shielding that can be obtained for pure beta emission is clear plastic. Using plastic shielding, the chemist has direct vision of the equipment and the reactions, thus eliminating some of the difficulties of remote control operation. The thickness of the shielding can be calculated from range data (see experiment 3). For safe operation a safety factor of at least twenty-five per cent should be included in calculating the thickness of the shield.

Shielding materials for gamma emitters may be as numerous as those used for beta emitters. However, the density and the thickness of the material are usually greater for gamma than for beta emitters. This follows from the fundamental precepts of absorption of beta and gamma rays. Beta rays have fairly well-defined ranges depending upon the density of the absorber; whereas gamma radiation is absorbed according to an exponential law as will be shown in the experiments to follow. Since gamma radiation is absorbed exponentially, it follows that both thickness and density are factors which must be considered whenever shielding must be used. Sometimes distance may be employed in place of shielding. If distance is to be the only shield, the inverse square law can be used to approximate the thickness of air or distance that needs to be interposed between the equipment and the operator. However, the usual conditions that exist are that the distance required will be so great that it will be virtually impossible to operate the equipment. Therefore, more dense materials must be used. Water, plastic, wood, or other lightweight materials cannot be used to advantage with most gamma radiation for the same reasons as given for air. Such materials as concrete, steel, or lead bricks are most often employed as shields for gamma radiation.

The thickness of the shield will depend, as has been mentioned, upon the density of the material used. Other factors are also involved as will be seen in the experimental section. Some of these factors are secondary radiation due to the absorption of the gamma and beta radiation in the shield, the atomic number of the material used, and the intensity of the radiation. The radiation intensity will be considered the most important since the amount of radiation to which the individual will be exposed and the extent of the shield will depend upon the total intensity at the source. This, of course, is considered only an approximation but will give a sufficiently valid result that the original intensity can be used to calculate the total thickness of the shield.

Several methods may be used to calculate the thickness of the shielding. The inverse square law may be used as has been mentioned above. The exponential absorption equation involving the use of the absorption coefficients for the material to be used for shielding is a valuable aid in determining the thickness of the shield. Several tables may be found in the literature from which the shielding thickness may be calculated under varying conditions. All of these methods consider the source as being an infinitely small point; however, the calculations are practical for broad sources which are normal in any operating process.

Since the intensity at the working surface is only approximate, it is always advisable to include a safety factor of ten in the calculations. That is, if the intensity desired at the working surface is 12.5 milliroentgens per hour, one should calculate the shielding to give 1.25 milliroentgens per hour.

As indicated above, gamma radiation calculations can become rather complex, particularly if all the factors involved are considered. For accurate values the energies of all the rays must be considered and all the mediums through which the rays will pass must be included—that is, the absorption in the liquid or solid containing the active material, the vessel in which it is contained, the air path between the vessel and the shield, the shielding material, and the air path between the shield and the operator. Also, since point sources are not the rule, the size of the source must be taken as a factor in the calculations. However, the approximations as noted above can be used provided that sufficient shielding will be utilized to reduce the total intensity outside the shield to a level well below tolerance.

To be effective, shielding must be placed on all sides of the source. That is, one must not consider that one is the only person to be within the range of the gamma rays issuing from a particular source. Walls, desk tops, ceilings, and floors are not always the best shields. Therefore, the six surfaces of a cube must be taken into consideration when shielding is provided. The amount of shielding necessary will, of course, depend upon the specific conditions as has been stated before. Even though calculations may show that shielding in some directions is not absolutely required, it is advisable to provide at least a minimum amount for safety. Since large solid shields are too bulky and heavy to manipulate, small bricks are usually used in building temporary shields. When bricks are to be used the cracks between the bricks should be completely closed in order to prevent stray beams. This may be brought about by the use of two layers of brick or by the use of interlocking bricks. The height of the shield will be determined by the intensity of the radiation behind the barricade. At no time should the operator allow his head to be in a field of radiation greater than that allowed by any other part of the shield.

The last statement immediately imposes conditions usually considered as remote control operation. That is, the manipulation of the equipment is done by the use of special tools and the operation is viewed through mirrors, periscopes, or columns of dense liquids set in the barricade. The latter two methods are often employed only in permanent type shielding, whereas the first method lends itself more readily to temporary shielding.

Before we leave the subject of shielding, the storage of radioisotopes should be considered. Every laboratory must have a well-shielded area wherein original shipments, dilutions to be used in various experiments, contaminated glassware, waste solutions and materials waiting for decay or disposal can be stored safely. The size of this area and the type of shielding provided will be dependent upon the extent of the facility. In some small establishments a well-shielded, unused hood may be sufficient, provided the hood can be securely fastened and is well marked as to its contents. At other installations rather large barricades, wells, or caves are in use. Whatever procedure is followed, the shielding provided must be adequate for the protection of anyone who may have business within the area.

The manner in which materials are stored may be left to the discretion of the particular laboratory. Regardless of the method that is used, a definite system and routine should be followed in order that anyone using the storage facilities may be able to determine the location of a particular item readily. Also the system should provide a simple procedure for taking an inventory of the stock on hand. Many systems are in use at present, and forms have been given which may be included as a part of any that may be devised. Some rapid positive means of identification of the individual items should be included as part of the system.

At the larger installations that have a segregated storage area, each individual laboratory should be provided with a small storage area in which process samples or original dilutions may be stored temporarily. At smaller installations this area may or may not be the same as the general storage area. In the latter case it would be desirable to keep the two areas separated; then only small amounts of active materials will be in the working area at any one time, thus reducing the hazards. In conjunction with the individual laboratory storage, a shielded sampling device should be provided. As has been discussed, the amount of shielding that is necessary will be controlled by the type of radiation involved, the amount of material, and the particular regulations concerning the laboratory. The sampling device may be entirely remote control and located behind heavy barricades, or it may be as simple as a syringe connected to a pipette by means of plastic tubing. In any case the student should be fully protected from direct or stray radiation when he is obtaining material for his experiment.

Transportation. Transportation of active materials around the laboratory should only be done in shielded containers. Depending upon the radiation involved, the equipment that will be necessary may be either rather simple or require a small hand truck. In either case the active material contained in a glass vessel should be inside a metal container which is provided with either ears or a bail for ease in handling. This inside metal container should then be placed inside the shield and the lid put in place before moving the assembly. The ears or bail on the inside container will simplify the handling of the activity because the unit may be readily moved safely behind shielding by means of simple tools that will engage with the ears or bail in a positive manner.

Accessories. It will be found by those who intend to have a tracer laboratory that the techniques involved when using radioactive materials are slightly more complicated than in the usual chemical laboratory. The chemist usually uses a pair of tongs to remove a beaker of boiling liquid from a hot plate; therefore he should certainly be able to use tongs to handle a beaker that contains a liquid that is thermally cold. The construction and use of tongs of various sizes and shapes can be left to the individual. Many of these are appearing on the market, but the average student or instructor will be able to devise and build all the necessary models in the laboratory shops. It should be stated that whatever is designed or built should have one feature in common. That is, every set of tongs should be so made that there is positive control of the apparatus to be moved. The average person is a little afraid of using tongs because he feels he does not have complete control of the material in the jaws. Once this feeling has been overcome the student will find that a pair of tongs is only an extension of his hand and that his physical person is thereby protected. Tongs can be made to reach over barricades, around corners, or even make two right angles without a great deal of difficulty. Other types of tongs can be used for handling different kinds of glassware. One important item that should be considered when designing tongs is that the jaws should be encased in some type of nonslip material. Plastic tubing is excellent for small tongs whereas asbestos cord or cloth may be used on larger varieties.

Waste containers, both metal and glass or crockery, must be provided in the laboratory. These should be distinctly marked for specific uses. That is, waste cans that will not be used for any active or contaminated materials may be painted with one color, whereas those that are to be used for contaminated substances only are painted with a brilliant or distinctive color. Regulations concerning these trash cans should be enforced for the protection of those who will use or handle them. Glass or crockery waste containers should be provided for storage of active liquids. These liquids may then be stored for decay or other future disposition unless the laboratory has other means for disposal of active wastes such that they may be cleaned every day or week. All these containers should be shielded or placed so that they may be easily accessible and at the same time the laboratory personnel is adequately protected.

Smaller pieces of equipment that will be useful in the active laboratory are too numerous to mention. Some of these are used in every chemical laboratory, whereas others may be peculiar to certain laboratories. In any case these articles should be shielded if necessary. One might consider in passing such items as a tray in which small equipment that has been used but not washed may be placed. This would help eliminate contamination of floors by preventing drops of active liquids. At the same time several pieces of equipment may be readily moved to the decontamination sink at the end of the experiment. It also provides a ready means for determining what equipment has been contaminated. Cleansing of pipettes in nitric acid is facilitated by using a tall cylinder with a plug of glass wool at the bottom into which used pipettes may be dropped. Tissue and paper towels are useful whenever a small piece of equipment must be set on the laboratory bench that is not otherwise protected. It will be left to the individual laboratories to devise other pieces of apparatus that will be useful in the active laboratory.

Counting Room. Whenever radioactive materials are used in experiments as tracers some method must be available whereby the activity may be determined accurately. The final counting is usually done in the counting room. The design and construction of the counting room may be varied widely, again depending upon the work that is to be accomplished by the laboratory. The walls may be made of thick concrete in order to eliminate as much stray or natural radiation as possible, or they may be constructed of simpler and cheaper materials. The best counting rooms will be surrounded by several inches of concrete. The walls and ceiling may be covered with acoustic board in order to reduce extraneous noises in the room.

Although Geiger-Mueller Counters may be operated in the normal laboratory, it is advisable to have the counting room air-conditioned. When constant temperature and humidity are maintained in the counting room, the accuracy of the counters is improved. At least, the results will be more reliable because temperature, pressure, and humidity changes will affect the counting rate due to changes in the air thickness between the tube and the sample mount. At the same time variable temperature may reduce the life of the tube, particularly if a very thin window tube is used.

Some scaling circuits are internally supplied with constant voltage regulators. If there is any doubt about the constancy of the line voltage to the instrument, a voltage regulation transformer should be installed in the room. Voltage changes on some scaling circuits may result in erroneous results, particularly if the plateau of the Geiger-Mueller tube is narrow.

The counting room should be supplied with small boxes into which the sample mounts may be slid for storage. However, these mounts should not be stored in the counting room longer than is necessary for the counting determination. If mounts are to be preserved for future reference, they should be stored in a protected area outside the counting room. All samples brought into the room should be placed in mount cases before they leave the tracer laboratory. Special areas should be provided for liquid counting apparatus and the apparatus must be shielded.

The floors of the counting room may be the same as for the rest of the laboratory. The desk tops do not have to be made of metal since all mounts will be protected before counting. Therefore, a smooth surface that may be easily washed is adequate. If the funds will allow, an air lock may be provided between the laboratory and the counting room. The room should be located as close to the tracer laboratory as possible in order to prevent contamination of other parts of the building. Of course, if the counting room is completely shielded, a ventilation system should be provided. This is usually done at the same time as the air-conditioning is installed. Frequently, when extreme accuracy is desired in the measurements, the counting room is electrically shielded to reduce stray radiation pulses.

Summary. Since this text has been primarily designed as a laboratory manual, not all of the details regarding the construction of the active laboratory have been thoroughly discussed. Enough has been presented so that those who are considering the installation of a tracer laboratory may be aware of the many pitfalls that are encountered. Before any construction has begun, it is advisable to obtain the advice of those who have operated tracer laboratories and to find out the problems that developed during and after the construction of other laboratories.

Those who plan to install active laboratories either for the instruction of radiochemical techniques or for the production of labeled compounds should not assume that the general type of laboratory described in this chapter is the only one. Several other types of laboratories have been constructed and have proved successful. Notable among these is the "Berkeley Dry Box" method which has one advantage in that all activities are kept inside a closed structure in a manner such that the bare hands cannot touch the equipment. There are some disadvantages to this method. Since the instructor will have to make the decision, he should carefully weigh all the advantages and disadvantages of all types of laboratories.

CHAPTER IV

WORKING IN A RADIOLABORATORY

WORKING IN A RADIOLABORATORY

Introduction. In the previous chapters the laboratory construction, the general operation of the tracer laboratory, and the health hazards related to radioactive materials have been considered. The discussion will now be concerned with the actual working in the laboratory. An attempt will be made to indicate the logical steps that must be followed in order that the student may protect himself and others and at the same time use radioactive isotopes as tracers. Perhaps the best way to do this will be to describe the various operations that are performed in an experiment.

Entering the Laboratory. As one approaches the tracer laboratory, the first thing that is noticed is the sign on the door stating: "RADIATION LABORATORY—NO ADMITTANCE WITHOUT PERMISSION." Every radiation laboratory should be posted in order to warn all persons of the dangers that might exist. Since the particular layout of each laboratory may be slightly different, we can only discuss the general path that a student will take when entering the laboratory. As one enters the building he may pass through areas that are restricted to nonactive chemical work and enter the change room which should separate the active from the nonactive laboratories. Street clothes should be removed and the special protective clothing put on. After the clothes have been changed, the student will not be allowed in the nonactive portions of the building.

Since several of the monitoring devices will be located in the change room, the student may check his person and clothes before entering and on leaving the laboratory. A record of these surveys should be made on the proper form and he should record the time he enters the laboratory. The film badges and personnel meters will be stored in a rack near the door to the active laboratory so that as the student passes through the door he may pick up the set assigned to him.

In the Laboratory. Working in the tracer laboratory requires constant vigilance by both the student and the instructor. The health and other hazards associated with radioactivity and laboratory work have been mentioned in earlier chapters. The application of the techniques that are involved in the safe operation of the laboratory and the experiments should be considered in relation to the hazards involved.

Before any attempt is made by the student to do experimental work, he should assemble all the equipment that will be needed. This equipment should be set up and any identification that is required placed on the apparatus. All chemicals or solutions that are required must be readily available and in sufficient quantity to allow at least one dry run (one without active material) before the active materials are used.

The equipment that is to be used in an experiment should be monitored carefully and any contaminated pieces placed in the contaminated glassware tray. After the equipment has been assembled it should be tested in order to be certain that valves work without sticking, that the vacuum lines are properly connected and adjusted, and that other operations can be done properly. A dry run should be made so that the student may become familiar with the actual operation. This procedure must be followed whenever any new or unusual reactions are to be made in order to determine what difficulties may arise during the active run. Many errors will often be found if the above procedure is followed. The more inactive runs that can be made, the less chance there will be for operating errors and the student will be thoroughly familiar with the equipment. It is realized that in a formal course there may be insufficient time to allow a series of dry runs to be made. If this is the case, only those experiments that have been included in other courses without active materials should be included in the tracer technique course. It should be noted that one of the reasons for the above procedure is to prevent the creation of hazardous situations by requiring that the student be thoroughly familiar with the equipment and the experiment.

After the equipment has been assembled and tested, the shielding that is necessary should be erected unless the apparatus has been installed in a permanent barricade. The course should be designed in order to acquaint the student with increasingly more difficult operations. Therefore, by the time the student is ready for remote control operations he should be able to operate the equipment without danger of exposure either to himself or others.

Only after the equipment has been set up, properly shielded, tested, and the student is familiar with its operation should any attempt to use radioactive materials be made. In order to provide a method of control, a set procedure should be followed in obtaining the active solutions or solids that are to be used. First the instructor should check the equipment, then the student will check the storage vault sheet to locate the particular material he needs. If the activity must be moved, the sample and its container should be placed in a covered shield. The student should record, on the forms provided, the data referring to the solution he has removed. When the material has been placed (in its shield) at the sampling device, then the student should put on rubber gloves.[1] From this time on he should be extremely careful in regard to touching anything in the laboratory that he might contaminate. The proper amount of material is transferred from the original solution to the vessel or bottle that will be used in the experiment. The original material must be returned to the vault and signed in, at the same time the amount that has been used must be recorded.

The material that has been obtained may be transferred to the equipment in several ways. Tongs may be used and the solution poured into the reaction vessel or vacuum may be applied to a portion of the equipment and the solution transferred. Whenever solutions or solids are moved in the open laboratory, they should be carried in special containers that do not permit the hands to come in contact with the vessel. Also all solutions should be in stoppered or screw cap bottles.

In all the above operations it is desirable to determine the radiation intensity. This can be done using any one of several instruments as indicated in a previous chapter. If any overtolerance conditions arise, the proper shielding should be provided. Throughout the experiment the student should assure himself that the radiation he is receiving is below tolerance by making surveys at critical points. If the maximum permissible rate of exposure is exceeded, then sufficient shielding should be provided.

During the performance of the experiment any samples that are required may be placed in suitable containers for future analysis. Any samples that are taken in this manner should be properly shielded before removal from the barricade. If it is required that the analysis take place

---

[1] Preferably the surgical type—see appendix.

immediately, the aliquot removed from the equipment is prepared for analysis behind the necessary shielding. The measurement of the activity may be performed in any one of several ways. Where large volumes or amounts that will exceed a predetermined tolerance are used, such as with annular volume tubes or dipping type Geiger Counters, this equipment should be shielded. If the equipment is not shielded and more than one set of equipment is available, the radiations from one in use will affect the readings on others. If mounts are prepared for direct counting it should be kept in mind that samples large enough to obtain valuable gamma counting data may have rather large concentrations of beta active materials and therefore should be handled with extreme caution. These mounts can and do show high radiation intensities since there is little or no absorbing material present, and the mount is more nearly a point source than the process material. The use of surgeons' gloves and tweezers for making up these mounts is highly advised in order to maintain as great a distance as possible and to absorb as much of the beta as possible in the rubber. Transporting and storing of mounts should be done in properly shielded boxes provided with shelves to separate the mounts. No high-level radioactive mounts should be left in the counting room for a longer time than that necessary for counting. These mounts should be treated and stored or destroyed in the same manner as any other active material.

If the counting or measurement of the activity can be left until after the experiment is completed, the equipment can be cleaned immediately after the procedure has been completed; if not, the cleaning must be done as soon as time permits. All solutions or solids are transferred to the proper waste containers and a decontaminating agent run through the equipment in order to remove the activity that might be left on the walls of the vessels. Radiation measurements on the various pieces of equipment must be made and the intensity must be well below tolerance before any of the equipment can be removed from the shield or the shield torn down. After the equipment has been thoroughly washed and monitored again it can be stored for future use.

There may be situations when it is undesirable to decontaminate the equipment after each run; however, these occasions will be rare and usually only when special research is in progress. Under such circumstances the equipment or barricade should be marked to indicate to everyone that radiation is present behind the barricade and the extent of the radiation. Also a notation should be made that the equipment is *not* to be operated by anyone other than the person who is using it. Special tags may be used for this purpose.

It has been mentioned that all equipment that has been used with active materials should be kept separated from all other equipment, and it is desirable to indelibly mark this equipment. In a larger laboratory that may be using greater amounts of certain activities it would be advisable to mark the equipment to indicate the particular type of activity for which it has been used. If this is done cross contamination should not occur. However such markings must not mean that equipment should not be cleaned as well as any other equipment. The only advantage that this suggestion has is that should any activity remain behind on the glass surfaces and not be found it will not seriously affect the next run. Also in small hospital laboratories identification of the equipment in this manner will reduce the possibility of giving a patient any other activity other than the one prescribed.

There are several situations that may not be readily obvious to the student whereby he may receive excess radiation. Although the radiation that is detectable through the side of a glass vessel may be very low, the student should remember that the radiation from the unprotected surface of the liquid will be much higher. Therefore, the surface of any active solutions or solids should not be in direct line with any portion of the body. Whenever active precipitates are made the same precaution should be observed. Also it should be pointed out that even though the solution from which the precipitate was made may not have been very active, the dried precipitate will be highly active due to the concentration effects. If precipitates are to be dried this should be done in a hood to prevent scattering of small particles in the laboratory. When dry powders are used particularly those containing carbon-14, calcium-45, or other long half-life activities that will become permanently fixed in the body, the student should wear a mask to prevent ingestion of any active particles. All those materials may best be handled in special hoods or dry boxes constructed particularly for this purpose.

Contaminated articles should not be carried into the counting room. All active mounts must be properly covered and sealed before they are counted. When samples are brought into the room in their containers, the container should be set on tissue or some disposable material in order to prevent contamination of the table or other surfaces. High-level samples must be well shielded and kept as far away from any counting equipment as possible, since radiation from this source may seriously affect the results of the experiment. When mounts are removed from the shield, they should be picked up with tweezers. The absorbers that are used in certain experiments must be handled carefully since these are easily contaminated, and most decontamination procedures will ruin the precision of the absorber. Also many of the absorbers are rather thin foils and can be damaged by rough treatment. The details of counting will be considered in the experiments presented in the next chapter.

Before leaving the laboratory, the student must clean up his working area, monitor, and decontaminate it if necessary. He must report any area that he cannot decontaminate easily or any hazardous situation that may exist. All survey data should be recorded on the proper forms. Approval of the survey by the supervisor must be obtained before leaving the laboratory.

Leaving the Laboratory. After a final check to be sure that all equipment has been washed or decontaminated, that gloves have been properly put away, and that the working areas are in order, the student will return to the change room where he will replace his meters in the proper rack and survey his clothes and himself. He should pay particular attention to his hands and shoes. The survey data are recorded on the forms provided and the time he leaves noted. Clothes are removed and a shower should be taken before putting on uncontaminated clothing. If coveralls or laboratory coats were used over the street clothes the latter should be very carefully surveyed and any radiation detected must be reported to the supervisor or instructor. It should be noted that the wearing of personal clothing in the active laboratory should be discouraged, as any contamination may be carried out and widely distributed depending upon where the clothing is washed or cleaned. If the contamination is serious it is possible that several unsuspecting people might be needlessly exposed. In order to eliminate this possibility all contaminated clothing should be washed by the laboratory, or at least under controlled conditions. If short-lived radioactive materials are used an alternative to washing is the storage of such clothing for a long enough time to allow for the decay of the activity.

Recording of experimental data may present certain problems in the active laboratory, since any notebooks that are used in the laboratory are likely to become contaminated. If the notebooks are not to leave the area, the problem is solved; however, the student usually needs the notebook in which he has recorded his data in order to write up the experiment. It is suggested that two notebooks be maintained, one for use in the laboratory and the other to be used for filing permanent data. The former should not leave the active laboratory and the data may be transcribed into the latter at a table set aside for this purpose in the change room. This procedure may seem to be stretching the point a little too far, but if one considers the extremely small amount of active material that is necessary to produce overtolerance radiation sources, particularly in a dry state, the suggestion does not appear to be as facetious as one would suppose.

Summary. In the first chapter the hazards of radioactive materials were considered. This was followed by chapters on the operation and construction of an active laboratory. The present chapter was devoted to a discussion of some of the methods that may be used in the tracer laboratory in order to prevent hazardous conditions. If the student has grasped all the ideas presented in these pages he should be prepared to follow the experiments in the next sections without danger to himself or to others. Above all the student should remember that "radiation need not be feared but that it must be respected."

References [2]

Radiation Hazards

W. Bloom, "Histological Changes Following Radiation Exposures," *Radiology* 49, 244 (1947).

Waldo E. Cohn, "Toxicity of Inhaled or Ingested Radioactive Products," *Nucleonics* 3, No. 1, 21 (1948).

C. L. Comar, "Radioisotopes in Nutritional Trace Element Studies—I," *Nucleonics* 3, No. 3, 32 (1948).

R. D. Evans, "Protection of Radium Dial Workers and Radiologists from Injury by Radium," *J. Ind. Hyg. Toxicol.* 25, 253 (1943).

G. Failla, "Biological Effects of Ionizing Radiations," *J. Applied Phys.* 12, 279 (1941).

R. E. Lapp and H. L. Andrews, "Health Physics," *Nucleonics* 3, No. 3, 60 (1948).

D. E. Lea, "Actions of Radiations on Living Cells," The Macmillan Co., New York, 1947.

H. Lisco, "Dosage Levels in Administration of Isotopes to Animals and Men," *U. S. Naval Med. Bull. Supp.*, Mar.-Apr., 161 (1948).

L. D. Marinelli, E. H. Quimby, and G. J. Hine, "Dosage Determination with Radioactive Isotopes—II," *Nucleonics* 2, No. 5 (Part I), 44 (1948).

L. D. Marinelli, E. H. Quimby, and G. J. Hine, "Dosage Determination with Radioactive Isotopes—II: Practical Considerations in Therapy and Protection," *Am. J. Roentgenol. Radium Therapy* 59, 260 (1948).

G. W. Morgan, "Gamma and Beta Shielding," *Atomic Energy Commission Isotopes Branch Circular B-3* (1948).

K. Z. Morgan, "Tolerance Considerations of Radioactive Substances," *J. Phys. Colloid Chem.* 51, 984 (1947).

K. Z. Morgan, "Health Physics and its Control of Radiation Exposures at Clinton Laboratory," *Chem. Eng. News* 25, 3794 (1947).

[2] MDDC refers to Manhattan District Declassified Code Documents.

K. Z. Morgan, "Hazards Presented by Radioactive Materials and How to Cope with Them," *U. S. Naval Med. Bull. Supp.*, Mar.-Apr., 142 (1948).

M. Nickson, "A Study of the Hands of Radiologists," MDDC-1309.

H. M. Parker, "Health Physics, Instrumentation, and Radiation Protection," MDDC-783.

J. R. Raper, "Effects of Total Surface Beta Irradiation," *Radiology* **49**, 314 (1947).

R. E. Rinaker, "Personnel Protection with Pocket Ionization Chambers." *Nucleonics* **2**, No. 1, 78 (1948).

"Safety Rules and Procedures Concerning Activity Hazards," MDDC-992.

Forrest Western, "Problems of Radioactive Disposal," *Nucleonics* **3**, No. 2, 43 (1948).

Bernard S. Wolf, "Medical Aspects of Radiation Safety," *Nucleonics* **3** No. 4, 25 (1948).

"Waste Disposal Symposium," *Nucleonics* **4**, No. 3, 9(1949).

G. W. Morgan, "Surveying and Monitoring of Radiation from Radioisotopes," *Nucleonics* **4**, No. 3, 24(1949).

Construction and Operation

Federal Register, *Vol. 12,* No. 220, pp. 7329-7333.

C. C. Gamertsfelder, "Gamma-ray Shielding Data," *Nucleonics* **3**, No. 4, 44 (1948).

F. C. Henriqués, Jr., A. P. Schrieber, "Administration and Operation of a Radiochemical Laboratory," *Nucleonics* **2**, No. 3, 1 (1948).

Henri A. Levy, "Design of Radiochemical Laboratories," *Chem. Eng. News* **24**, 3168 (1946).

W. H. Sullivan, "Control of Radioactivity Hazards," *Chem. Eng. News* **25**, 1862 (1947).

J. Swartout, "Design of Radiochemistry Laboratories with Low Levels of Radioactivity," MDDC-1717.

P. C. Tompkins, "Laboratory Handling of Radioactive Material: Protection of Personnel and Equipment," *U. S. Naval Med. Bull. Supp.,* Mar-Apr., 164 (1948).

P. C. Tompkins, "Laboratory Handling of Radioactive Material," MDDC-1414.

P. C. Tompkins, A. Broido, and J. D. Teresi, "The Handling of Radioactive Materials in the Experimental Biology Section," MDDC-377.

P. C. Tompkins and H. A. Levy, "Influence of Radioactivity on Chemical Laboratory Technique and Design," MDDC-1719.

The Experiments. The exercises which follow have been designed with several specific aims in mind. First, the student is introduced progressively to more complex manipulations. Secondly, even though shielding may be used by the supervisor to prepare the stock radioactive solutions from the Oak Ridge shipment, little or no shielding is required for the very small amounts of activity used in most of the experiments. Thirdly, a wide enough variety of exercises is included so that a course can be arranged to meet almost any type of demand.

CHAPTER V

BASIC EXPERIMENTS

EXPERIMENTS

CHAPTER V

BASIC EXPERIMENTS

I. THE LAURITSEN ELECTROSCOPE

OBJECT

This experiment is designed to illustrate the operation and use of the Lauritsen Electroscope as a radiation detector. Background measurements are made, the linear range of the scale is determined, and the sensitivity of the instrument is calculated.

THEORY

When a particle produces ionization in a gas, current will flow between two charged electrodes placed in the gas. The magnitude of the current flowing can be directly related to the number of ions reaching the electrodes. A simple instrument illustrating this phenomenon is the ordinary gold-leaf electroscope. When such an apparatus is charged, the leaves will diverge. But, if the gas surrounding the leaves becomes ionized, the leaves will collapse due to a flow of current which causes a neutralization of charge. The ionization current is measured by the rate of discharge of the leaves and can be in turn related to the number of incoming particles.

The Lauritsen Electroscope, shown in Figure 2, is a quartz fiber instrument very similar in operation and basic construction to the gold-leaf electroscope, but having a greater sensitivity. It is a dependable and practical radiation measuring device, widely used in tracer work. Ordinarily the instrument is employed only for gamma and strong beta rays, but it can be adapted to alpha and weak beta particles by the use of specially constructed thin lacquer or aluminum windows. For neutron work the chamber is lined with boron, paraffin, or other suitable materials.

The very thin gold-sputtered quartz fiber (so treated to render it conducting) is fastened to the metal wire supported inside the ionization chamber by an amber insulator.

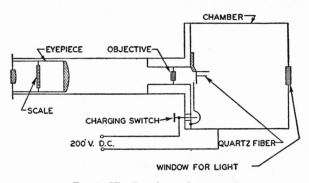

FIG. 2. The Lauritsen electroscope.

Upon charging the system to a potential of approximately 200 volts with the charger, the quartz fiber will bend away from its metal support. The fiber's position may be read through the eyepiece on the 100-division scale. Any ionization produced in the chamber by entering radiation will cause the charge to leak off the wire-fiber system, tending to return the fiber to its original uncharged position. The rate of movement can be measured and related directly to the strength of the entering radiation.

The quartz fiber and the wire are extremely small and have a capacity of 10^{-13} farads. The collection of 10^6 ion pairs in the chamber produces a scale deflection of approximately one division. This indicates that the sensitivity of the instrument is about one to four scale divisions per milli-curie at a distance of one meter or 10^5 roentgens per division.

The scale is almost, but not quite, linear. For this reason, it is necessary to calibrate it to determine the usable portion, which is generally linear within one per cent for a region of fifty to seventy scale divisions.

There is always a background rate associated with an electroscope due to leakage across the insulation, ionization produced by cosmic radiation, and contamination of the instrument and its surroundings. The cosmic ray contribution may be minimized by heavy lead shielding, and the portion of the background rate due to contamination may be reduced by utmost care on the part of the operator. The total background may vary from day to day, and therefore it must be determined at frequent intervals. It generally has a value of from 1.5 to six scale division per hour.

The Lauritsen Electroscope gives readings reproducible to about 0.5 per cent over any given scale range. In spite of the delicacy of the quartz fiber, the instrument is very rugged and can be carried about without too great fear of damage. Only experienced persons, however, should attempt to remove the chamber, since this exposes the quartz fiber.

APPARATUS AND MATERIALS

Lauritsen Electroscope with source of light and charger, stop watch, solution 0.01 molar in disodium hydrogen phosphate containing two to three millicuries of phosphorus-32 per liter,[1] 0.1 milliliter pipette and syringe to fit, infrared lamp, aluminum foil six mils thick, cardboard mounting

[1] See Chapter IX.

cards, holder to retain cardboard mounting cards in a constant geometry, cellophane, Scotch tape.

PROCEDURE

Charging the Electroscope. A special rectifier unit mounted along with the electroscope is used to supply the charging voltage. This unit operates from the 110-volt A.C. line, and the D.C. voltage to be applied to the electroscope is controlled by a knob on the top of the rectifier housing. This knob also acts as the on-off switch.

With the knob turned to the extreme counterclockwise position, which is the off position, plug the unit into the 110-volt A.C. line outlet. Turn the switch just on and allow the instrument to warm up for at least two minutes; after which, turn the knob to the position marked four. Depress the charging button momentarily and then release it. Look through the eyepiece and observe whether the fiber is on the scale or not. If not, advance the control knob one-half unit and repeat the charging procedure. Continue in this fashion until the fiber appears on the scale. Then by successive momentary depressions of the charging button bring the fiber to a position between zero and one on the scale. If the charging operation should throw the fiber beyond the zero point, allow the instructor to rapidly discharge the instrument with a fairly strong radioactive source.

Background Measurement. Charge the electroscope to about thirty on the scale and then allow it to stand for about five minutes. Then record the position of the fiber on the scale estimating the reading to 0.1 division, and simultaneously start the stop watch. Allow to discharge for forty minutes. Repeat this procedure after charging the instrument to about ten on the scale.

Sample Preparation. Cut a small square of aluminum

foil about four centimeters on a side. Practice the delivery of a 0.1 milliliter sample of water with the pipette several times, then deliver exactly 0.1 milliliter of the radiophosphorus solution onto the foil. Place the aluminum foil under an infrared lamp and allow the solution to evaporate to dryness, taking care to avoid spattering. Center the prepared sample on a cardboard mounting card, cover with cellophane, and fasten with Scotch tape. Measure the activity of the sample with the electroscope, recording the scale reading every ten seconds for a period of sixty seconds. A discharge rate of from 0.3 to one division per second should be observed. If the rate is greater than this, dilute the radioactive solution with an appropriate amount of water and prepare a new sample. If the rate is less, evaporate on the original foil a second 0.1-milliliter portion of the active material. After readjustment of the activity by one of the above procedures, repeat the discharge rate experiments.

Determination of Scale Linearity. With the sample prepared in the previous section determine the time required for discharge in each ten-division portion of the scale.

Measurement of Samples. Measure and record the activity of the prepared sample twice in the linear region of the scale. Then prepare samples using 0.2, 0.3, 0.4, and 0.5 milliliter portions of the radioactive phosphate solution by successive addition and evaporation operations on the original sample. Measure and record the activity of each of these samples twice. Under the instructor's supervision place the radioactive samples in the waste container provided for them.

Calculations and Questions

1. Average the two background determinations and express the result in divisions per hour and divisions per second.

2. Construct a plot of the discharge rate observed as a function of the region of the scale.

3. Construct a plot of the discharge rate as a function of relative sample strength, taking into consideration the background rate.

4. Assuming the absolute sample strength to be two microcuries per milliliter, calculate the sensitivity of the instrument in divisions per microcurie per second.

5. The formation of a pair of ions in air required on the average about thirty-five electron volts. If ten thousand 0.7 million electron volt beta particles expend one-half their energy in the chamber of a Lauritsen Electroscope, how many scale divisions will the quartz fiber be deflected?

6. Diagram and explain the operation of a vacuum tube electrometer.

References

C. C. Lauritsen and T. Lauritsen, *Rev. Sci. Instruments* 8, 438 (1937).

E. C. Pollard and W. L. Davidson, *"Applied Nuclear Physics,"* John Wiley and Sons, Inc., New York, 1942, pp. 18-23.

J. Strong, H. V. Neher, A. E. Whitford, C. H. Cartwright, and R. Hayward, "Procedures in Experimental Physics," Prentice-Hall, Inc., New York, 1944, pp. 217-258.

II. The Geiger-Mueller Counter

OBJECT

The purpose of this experiment is to demonstrate the operation and characteristics of the Geiger-Mueller Counter. The operating plateau, background, sample holder step factor, and coincidence correction are determined. The sensitivity of the counter is measured with a standard radioactive sample as a comparison.

THEORY

The Complete Counter Circuit. The Geiger-Mueller Counter is the most generally used device for the detection and determination of beta radiation. Its advantages are its high sensitivity, in that it will detect single particles, and its resolving time, in that it will measure separate ionizing events coming very close together. The disadvantages are that it has a very complex electrical circuit giving rise to the possibility of breakdown in any of the many elements, and the accuracy of this instrument is determined by the background counting rate accompanying a sample determination. The major elements of a typical Geiger-Mueller Counter circuit are shown in Figure 3, and the main units

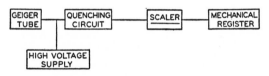

FIG. 3. Geiger-Muller counter circuit.

in the immediate electrical connections to the Geiger tube are shown in Figure 4.

The Geiger tube usually consists of a cylindrical glass envelope lined with a thin layer of metal and a central wire coaxial with and insulated from the outer cylinder. The tube is sealed and contains a gas or mixture of gases at low pressure. When a particle enters the tube, it produces a

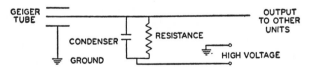

FIG. 4. Geiger tube connections.

few ion pairs, consisting of electrons and positively charged ions. Under the influence of the applied electrical field, the electrons move toward the wire at a rate much greater than that of the positive ions which move toward the metal wall. The acceleration of the electrons by the field causes them to collide with many other particles producing further ionization. This gives an avalanche of electrons, causing a discharge pulse to be sent out to the other units.

Due to the sluggishness of the positive ions, a positive space charge remains around the wire. In addition to this, the positive ions may produce photons on striking the metal wall. In order for the tube to be able to end one pulse and to initiate another output pulse, the positive ions must drift to the wall, requiring 10^{-3} to 10^{-4} seconds. This is termed the "dead time" since no other particle can be detected in its duration. Two methods are available for "quenching" the tube—that is, restoring it to normal in a very short time. The first of these is the addition of a polyatomic gas to the gas in the tube. The excess energy in the tube after an ionizing event is quickly taken up by decomposition of these molecules. Another method is the insertion of a special unit into the series of units in the total circuit. This quenching circuit tends to decrease the voltage momentarily at the Geiger tube, quenching the current and re-establishing the original conditions.

In the majority of cases it is desirable to count impulses at the rate of several thousand per minute. Since most mechanical recorders are not constructed to do this, a scaler is interposed between the counter itself and the register. This scaler transmits one pulse to the register when some preassigned number of pulses has come through from the Geiger tube. The high voltage supply and mechanical register are ordinary commercial instruments. Frequently all of these separate units or any combination of them are built into one housing.

Operation and Corrections. When the impressed voltage in the tube is low, the pulse given by ionizing particles is too weak to be detected. As the voltage is increased, the "threshold" or the voltage value at which counts begin to register is reached. Further increase in voltage produces an increase in the number of counts detected until finally a voltage region is reached in which practically all the pulses are detected. Following this "plateau" at voltage values somewhat higher the tube goes into continuous discharge. The tube is operated at the voltage indicated by the center of the plateau, where the number of counts per unit time is independent of applied voltage. At this point, considerable variations in the voltage will not introduce error into determinations of activity.

There are several methods for the determination of the dead time. The first of these is to construct a plot of known sample concentration against observed counts per unit time. At some value of counts per unit time, the expected straight line begins to curve away due to particles entering the tube during the dead time. Corrections may be applied by referring the observed number of counts back to the extrapolated straight line. A more accurate procedure is to prepare two sources of approximately the same counting rate, usually about 5,000 counts per minute. They are counted separately giving counting rates of C_1 and C_2, and then together giving a counting rate of C_3. The resolving time T is given by the equation:

$$T = \frac{2(C_1 + C_2 - C_3)}{(C_1 + C_2)C_3}$$

The resolving time may then be related to the true counting rate N_T and the apparent counting rate N_A by:

$$N_T = N_A e^{-N_A T}$$

Every Geiger-Mueller Counter will give a background counting rate due to cosmic rays, contamination, and circuit peculiarities. The effect due to the first two causes may be reduced by heavy lead shielding, clean instruments, and good workmanship. Correction for the background may be made by determining the background count without any radioactive sample near, and then subtraction of this value from all sample measurements.

A counter may give a count of 1,000 counts per minute on a certain sample, and then one half-life later, a count of 510 counts per minute is observed. This is due to varying efficiency of the counter. A long-lived radioactive standard giving a constant count is usually prepared or purchased and used to correct the readings.

All samples should be measured in the same geometry and under the same conditions with particular respect to the area of the window through which the radiation enters, the distance from the sample to the tube, the area of the sample, and the mounting material used.

The thicknesses of all materials, including the counter tube window, placed between the sample and the sensitive volume of the tube must be taken into consideration. In addition, materials themselves will absorb their own radioactive particles.

Statistics of Counting. Radioactive decay is a random process, and therefore according to the laws of probability, the greater the number of counts observed, the more accurate will be the measured rate.

The standard deviation D is defined as the number of counts a particular result may be in error, either plus or minus. For very large counts, this value is simply the square root of the number of counts N, or

$$D = \sqrt{N}$$

When the count of the sample plus the background N_s is of the same order as the count of the background alone N_B, then the standard deviation is the square root of the sums of the individual standard deviations squared, or

$$D_s = \sqrt{N_s}$$
$$D_B = \sqrt{N_B}$$
$$\text{TOTAL} = \sqrt{D_s^2 + D_B^2} = \sqrt{N_s + N_B}$$

The probable error P is the error such that the number of errors greater than it is equal to the number of errors less than it. In other words, it is the expected error. Its value is smaller than the standard deviation by a factor of 0.6745, or

$$P = 0.6745\,D$$

APPARATUS AND MATERIALS

Geiger-Mueller Counter, with a tube having a wall thickness of two to four milligrams per square centimeter, radioactivity standard, solution 0.01 molar disodium hydrogen phosphate containing two to three millicuries of phosphorus-32 per liter,[1] stop watch, sample holder having several shelves, 0.1 milliliter pipette with syringe, infrared lamp, squares of aluminum foil six mils thick, cardboard mounting cards to fit the sample holder, cellophane, Scotch tape.

PROCEDURE

Determination of the Operating Voltage. After properly connecting up the various units in the Geiger-Mueller

[1] See Chapter IX.

Counter and making sure that all switches are off, plug the instrument into the 110-volt A.C. line, turn on the master switch and allow the instrument to warm up for at least two minutes. If there is a scale selector, use it to actuate the scale. Place the radioactive standard on a cardboard mounting card and secure it in place with Scotch tape; set it on the top shelf of the sample holder. After the warmup period turn on the high voltage switch, wait one minute, and then turn on the count switch. Gradually increase the voltage until counts start to be registered. Record this value as the threshold potential. Increase the voltage in steps of twenty-five volts and take a count each time for a long enough time to insure at least 5,000 counts being registered. The total number of counts is equal to the register reading multiplied by the scaling factor plus the interpolator value. Record the number of counts and the time at each setting; then express the results as counts per minute. Continue this procedure up to and through the region where the counting rate is constant, and then until the rate shows a marked increase, indicating that the usable operating region has been passed. Immediately decrease the voltage seventy-five volts to prevent possible damage to the tube. Determine the center of the plateau and use this voltage as the operating voltage for all future determinations on this counter. If any unit in the total circuit is replaced or altered, a new plateau determination must be made. Even if no changes are made, it is advisable to re-determine the operating voltage before each period of use.

Determination of Background. Take two ten-minute counts with no radioactive sample near the counter. Average these counts and apply this as a correction to all subsequent measurements.

Determination of Sample Holder Shelf Factor. Count

the radioactive standard for five minutes on each sample holder shelf.

Determination of a Sample. Dilute 0.1 milliliter of the radio-phosphorus solution with four milliliters of water and mix thoroughly. Cut a small square of aluminum foil about four centimeters square. Evaporate 0.1 milliliter of the prepared active solution on this foil, place the sample on a cardboard mounting card, cover with a piece of cellophane, and fasten securely with Scotch tape. Take a count for five minutes on this sample placed in the top shelf of the sample holder.

Determination of Dead Time Correction. Evaporate successive 0.1 milliliter portions of the prepared radioactive phosphate solution on the same sample used above, taking a count for five minutes between each addition. Continue to add active material to the sample until the observed activity is less than that theoretically computed from the first sample by twenty per cent. Under the instructor's supervision place the radioactive samples in the waste container provided for them.

Calculations and Questions

1. Make a plot of the counts per minute of the radioactive standard versus the applied voltage.

   (a) What is the length of the plateau? (b) What is the percentage increase in counting rate per 100 volts on the plateau? (c) What is the operating voltage for the counter?

2. Calculate the shelf factors between the lower shelves and the top shelf.

3. Assume that the properties of the radiation from the phosphorus solution residue and the radiation from the radioactivity standard are the same.

   (a) Calculate the strength of the phosphorus solution in millicuries per milliliter. (b) What fraction of the beta particles emitted by the sample were detected?

4. (a) Construct a graph plotting counts per minute against the number of portions of radiophosphorus solution determined. (b) Make a plot of the dead time correction factor versus the observed counting rate.

5. Calculate the standard deviation for all measurements.

6. Calculate the discharge rate which could be observed on the electroscope from a sample giving 1,000 counts per minute on the counter.

7. Draw the circuit diagrams for a scale-of-two-scaler and a quenching circuit. Briefly describe the operation of both.

References

J. Strong, H. V. Neher, A. E. Whitford, C. H. Cartwright, and R. Hayward, "Procedures in Experimental Physics," Prentice-Hall, Inc., New York, 1944, pp. 259-304.

E. C. Pollard and W. L. Davidson, "Applied Nuclear Physics," John Wiley and Sons, Inc., New York, 1942, pp. 26-39.

M. D. Kamen, "Radioactive Tracers in Biology," Academic Press, Inc., New York, 1947, pp. 58-94.

J. M. Cork, "Radioactivity and Nuclear Physics," D. Van Nostrand Co., Inc., 1947, pp. 37-45.

S. A. Korff, "Electron and Nuclear Counters," D. Van Nostrand Co., Inc., 1946, pp. 6-14, 61 ff.

S. C. Brown, *Nucleonics* 2, No. 6, 10-22 (1948).

S. C. Brown, *Nucleonics* 3, No. 2, 50-64 (1948).

III. Characteristics of Beta Particles (One Source)

OBJECT

In this experiment some of the most important characteristics of beta particles are studied. The absorption is measured, the approximate range is determined, and the phenomenon of back-scattering is illustrated with several different backing materials.

Absorption and Range Determination. A very important factor to be considered when choosing a radioactive isotope for tracer work is the penetrating power of the emitted radiation. For radioactive substances emitting low energy particles, the problems of sample preparation and detection are quite complicated. Even with high energy particles consideration must be made of the absorption by thin layers of material. Since beta particles are the most frequently utilized, this experiment will deal with their characterization.

Experimentally it has been found that the beta particles from a radioactive substance give a range distribution which closely resembles an exponential curve. This effect has been explained as a result of two phenomena. An electron passing through matter is deflected by numerous collisions, leading to much straggling, and the energy spectrum of beta particles emitted from a nucleus is not monochromatic, but has a Maxwellian distribution.

There are two main processes by which the energy of a beta particle may be lost. When a beta particle is de-accelerated in the atomic field of a nucleus, radiation which is called bremsstrahlung is emitted. The beta particle also loses energy in collision with other electrons, producing ionization. Each ion pair produced requires about twenty-five electron volts of energy. The ratio of ionization loss to radiative loss is given roughly by the relation

$$\frac{820}{ZE}$$

in which Z is the atomic number of the absorber and E is the energy of the beta particle in million electron volts. It can be seen that radiative losses become appreciable only for high energy beta particles.

Many attempts have been made to formulate an empirical relation between the range of beta particles and their energy. No satisfactory equation has as yet been found, but the following equations seem to apply in various ranges.

For beta particles whose energy is greater than 0.8 Mev

$$R_{max} = 542 E_{max} - 133$$
$$\text{(in Mev)}$$

For beta particles whose energy is between 0.15 and 0.8 Mev

$$R_{max} = 407 E_{max}^{1.38}$$
$$\text{(in Mev)}$$

For beta particles whose energy is below 0.2 Mev

$$R_{max} = \frac{E_{max}^{5/3}(\text{in Kev})}{150}$$

In all of these formulas R_{max} is the maximum range in milligrams per square centimeter and E_{max} is the maximum energy of the beta particles. It is approximately true that the stopping power per unit mass is the same for all substances.

The thickness G in grams per square centimeter of an absorber can be related to the number of particles coming through the absorber N by the relation

$$\frac{N}{N_0} = e^{-\mu G}$$

where N_0 is the number of particles observed without an absorber and μ is the absorption coefficient. The coefficient

μ can be approximately related to the maximum energy of the beta particles by the expression

$$\mu = \frac{22}{E_{max}^{4/3}}$$

The true range of beta particles is not easy to determine because of the difficulty of establishing the absorber thickness at which the transmission becomes zero, since the very penetrating bremsstrahlung is emitted even when all the beta particles are being absorbed. An additional factor frequently influencing absolute range value is the unknown thickness of the counter window and the air between sample and window.

Back Scattering. Most tracer work involves the comparison of two or more radioactive samples. In order to obtain an accurate result, all samples must be prepared so that the observed activity is a true indication of the actual disintegration rate. The scattering of beta particles by the backing material of a sample has a large effect on the observed activity and must be considered in all tracer work.

The scattering of beta particles is a result of collisions both with nuclei and other electrons. The probability of scattering by the nucleus increases proportionally as the atomic number squared, and by the orbital electrons as the atomic number. Hence, scattering will be much greater in the elements of high atomic number. The back-scattering also increases as the thickness of the backing material increases up to one-half the range of the particle. The per cent of back-scattering B is calculated from the following formula

$$B = \frac{100\,(N - N_0)}{N_0}$$

N_0 being equal to the activity of the sample mounted on an extremely low atomic number material, and N the activity of the sample with a backing material. This experiment is not designed as an accurate measure of scattering but merely to demonstrate the relations between back-scattering, thickness, and atomic number.

APPARATUS AND MATERIALS

Geiger-Mueller Counter with a tube having a wall thickness of two to four milligrams per square centimeter, stop watch or clock in circuit, solution 0.01 molar disodium hydrogen phosphate containing three to four millicuries of phosphorus-32 per liter,[1] sample holder having several shelves, 0.1 milliliter pipette with syringe, infrared lamp, squares of aluminum foil four centimeters on a side and of several different known thicknesses (two to six millimeters), set of absorbers, cardboard mounting cards to fit sample holder, cellophane, Scotch tape, squares of glass, polystyrene, and several metals (four centimeters on an edge) having approximately the same thickness in milligrams per square centimeter.

PROCEDURE

Absorption and Range Determination. Prepare a sample of radioactive phosphorus in a manner analogous to that described in the experiment on the Geiger-Mueller Counter which will give approximately 10,000 counts per minute on the second shelf of the sample holder. Make certain that the sample is completely covered with cellophane and that the mounting card is not contaminated.

Take a background count and sample count from the second shelf without an absorber. Then insert each absorber in the top shelf, beginning with the thinnest, and

[1] See Chapter IX.

take a long enough count so that at least 5,000 total counts are registered, preferably 10,000. The sample should not be moved throughout these measurements.

Back-Scattering Determinations. Evaporate 0.1 milliliter of the radiophosphorus solution to dryness in the center of each of the backing materials. Place each sample activity upward in the center of a cardboard mounting card, cover it with cellophane, and secure this in place with Scotch tape. Measure the activity of each of the prepared phosphorus deposits taking at least 5,000 counts in every instance.

Calculations and Questions

1. Construct a graph plotting sample activity on a log scale versus the absorber thickness in milligrams per square centimeter on a linear scale.

(a) From the graph determine what appears to be the range of the beta particles. (b) How does this range compare with that calculated from the equation as given in the Theory section, using 1.69 Mev as the maximum energy of the phosphorus-32 beta particles? (c) From the answers to parts (a) and (b), calculate the thickness in milligrams per square centimeter of the counter window and the air in between the sample and the sensitive volume.

2. Calculate the absorption coefficient, μ, and the linear absorption coefficient $\mu\rho$ (where ρ is the density of the absorber) for the linear portion of the absorption curve. How does this compare with the mass absorption coefficient calculated from the maximum energy of phosphorus-32 beta particles?

3. Calculate the standard deviation and probable error for the count obtained with the thickest absorber in place.

4. Calculate the per cent of back-scattering for each sample, using the polystyrene or the thinnest aluminum backed sample as the no-backing measurement.

Other Suggested Experiments

Characterization of complex beta decay emitters.

References

F. Rasetti, "Elements of Nuclear Physics," Prentice-Hall, Inc., New York, 1936, pp. 63-74.

G. Hevesy and F. A. Paneth, "A Manual of Radioactivity," Oxford University Press, London, 1938, pp. 36-48.

M. D. Kamen, "Radioactivity Tracers in Biology," Academic Press Inc., New York, 1947, pp. 42-52.

J. M. Cork, "Radioactivity and Nuclear Physics," D. Van Nostrand Co., Inc., New York, 1947, pp. 116-138.

L. E. Glendenin, *Nucleonics* 2, No. 1, 12-27 (1948).

IV. Measurement of Radioactive Liquids

OBJECT

In this experiment, several useful methods for measuring the activity of liquids will be illustrated. In addition, the effect of density upon the accuracy of radiosolution measurements will be demonstrated.

THEORY

Solution measurements are very satisfactory in the assay of radioactive materials. The preparation of samples and the reproducibility of geometry is much simpler than in the case of solid materials. The self-absorption effects encountered in solids are greatly simplified in solution counting. In determinations involving liquid samples, the adjustment of activity can be readily made by dilution or concentration. The four types of solution counting apparatus that have been widely employed are cylindrical Geiger-Mueller tubes with an annular volume container, cylindrical or end-window Geiger-Mueller tube with a flat solution container, dipping Geiger-Mueller Counters and a liquid container to fit, and cylindrical or end-window counters placed over an open dish containing the solution.

In all types of apparatus, the same volume of solution, the same counter, the same container, and the same geometry must be used in measuring all samples to be compared. The density also plays a role in the accuracy of the determinations and all samples should be of approximately the same density.

The Annular Volume Counting Apparatus. The annular volume counting apparatus is illustrated in Figure 5. It consists of a cylindrical Geiger-Mueller counting tube having a wall thickness of about thirty milligrams per square centimeter. Constructed to fit around this tube is an annular volume container, having an inner wall thickness of one-fortieth to one-thirty-second of an inch, with two glass stoppers to facilitate filling, emptying, and cleaning. The Geiger-Mueller tube is secured in a suitable support which also serves as a holder to maintain the sample container in constant geometry. Generally, a scratch or mark is placed on one of the filling arms of the container to allow the apparatus to be filled with the same volume for each determination.

The Flat Solution Container Apparatus. Two arrangements for this method are shown in Figure 6, one employing the -cylindrical counting tube, and the other using the end-window counting tube. These tubes usually have

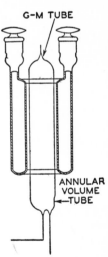

G-M TUBE

ANNULAR VOLUME TUBE

Fig. 5.

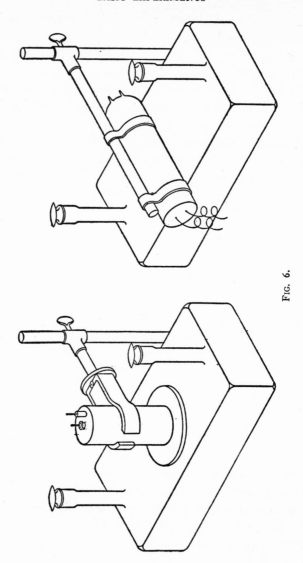

FIG. 6.

wall and window thickness of thirty milligrams per square centimeter and two to four milligrams per square centimeter respectively. The flat solution container has two filling stoppers and the upper surface has a thickness of one-fortieth to one-thirty-second of an inch. As in the annular volume tube, one of the arms has a scratch or mark placed upon it to simplify filling accuracy.

The Dipping Counter Apparatus. In Figure 7, the dipping counter and its solution cell are illustrated. Several different companies are now manufacturing these counters for the commercial market. The sample holder is constructed to contain from fifteen to twenty milliliters of solution. Frequently the volume of the solution is measured before placing it in the container but in some cases a mark or scratch on the wall indicates the volume. Care must be exercised to see that the counting tube is always immersed to the same depth and that the tube is centered in the container.

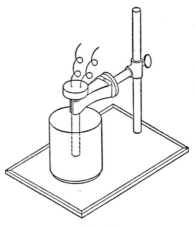

Fig. 7.

Open Solution Counting Apparatus. Figure 8 shows two arrangements employed for counting solutions in open Petri dishes, one with a cylindrical tube and one with an end-window tube. Again, as with the previous arrangements, constant geometry must be maintained.

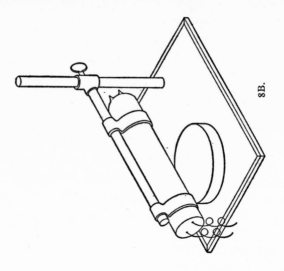

8B.

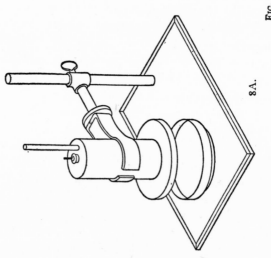

8A.

Fig. 8.

APPARATUS AND MATERIALS

Geiger-Mueller Counter, several types of liquid counting apparatus, one liter of solution containing one millicurie of phosphorus-32 per liter,[1] 0.1 milliliter pipette, ten fifty-milliliter volumetric flasks, solution of sodium nitrate containing 100 grams per liter.

PROCEDURE

Introduce into a fifty-milliliter volumetric flask 0.1 milliliter of the radioactive phosphorus solution, dilute to volume with water, and shake well. Repeat this operation using 0.3 milliliter, 0.5 milliliter, 0.7 milliliter, and one milliliter of the active material. Using one of the methods for liquid counting, measure the activities of each of these solutions, returning the solutions to their proper containers after the determination. Utilizing each of the remaining counting arrangements, repeat the activity measurements.

Into each of four fifty-milliliter volumetric flasks, place 0.5 milliliter of the radioactive solution. Into the first flask pipette exactly ten milliliters of the sodium nitrate solution, twenty milliliters into the second, thirty milliliters into the third, and forty milliliters into the fourth. Fill each of the flasks to the mark with water, and mix well. Using two of the solution counting procedures, measure the activities of these four solutions by each method.

Calculations and Questions

1. For each method construct a graph plotting sample strength against activity.

[1] See Chapter IX.

2. Construct a chart comparing the methods as to efficiency, accuracy, ease of operation, and sensitivity. Which method do you consider the best? Why?

3. Discuss briefly the errors involved in solution measurements.

4. Calculate for each arrangement the energy a 1.69 Mev beta particle will have when it reaches the sensitive volume of the counting tube, considering that it leaves the center of the solution.

5. Construct a graph for each method used, plotting density against activity.

6. Suggest a method by which density corrections may be made. How may density corrections be avoided?

References

W. F. Bale, F. L. Haven, and M. L. Lefevre, *Rev. Sci. Instr.* **10**, 193 (1939).

A. K. Solomon and J. D. Ester, *Rev. Sci. Instr.* **19**, 47 (1948).

H. A. C. McKay, *Rev. Sci. Instr.* **32**, 103 (1941).

F. Van Hecke, *Ann. Sci. Bruxelles,* Ser. I, **60**, 224 (1946).

C. L. Comar, *Nucleonics* **3**, No. 3, 37 (1948).

V.   Determination of Low Energy Beta Particles

OBJECT

The complexities introduced by self-absorption into the determination of low energy beta particles are to be studied. Measurements are made on barium sulfate samples containing radioactive sulfur. The thicknesses of these samples are related to the measured activities and the "infinite thickness" value is determined.

THEORY

Frequently the radioscientist finds that the radioisotope he desires to measure emits very soft beta particles. The most important of these are carbon-14 and sulfur-35, emitting betas having maximum energies of 140 Kev and 170 Kev respectively. In the measurement of these low energy particles several absorption factors must be considered. The sample must be placed close to the counter window to minimize air-path absorption; the counter window must be as thin as possible to minimize absorption therein; and the error due to absorption of the radiations in the sample material itself (self-absorption) must be taken into account.

Several procedures have been used to correct for self-absorption. Samples have been prepared in very thin layers so that the absorption is very small. The difficulty in this procedure is that the samples must be of high specific activity, or else considerable error will be introduced. In addition to this, attempts have been made to prepare all samples with a constant thickness. This procedure is not easy to realize, since there is considerable difficulty attached to the preparation of homogeneous samples of a given thickness. Probably the best procedure in use at present is the mounting and measurement of samples of an "infinite thickness." An "infinite thickness" is a thickness such that the radiation from the bottom of the sample is completely absorbed by the sample itself. Therefore, a determination on an infinitely thick sample is a true measure of its activity relative to any other infinitely thick sample. This method is applicable in almost all cases except when the amount of sample available is too small.

If the activities of several constant area samples of a weak beta-emitting substance are plotted against their thicknesses, a curve similar to the one shown in Figure 9 can be drawn through the points. It will be noted that the activity approaches a maximum which occurs at the minimum infinite thickness value. All samples thicker than this value will have the same measured activity. This curve can be represented within two to five per cent by the equation:

$$\frac{A_0}{A_E} = 1 - e^{-\frac{bX}{R}}$$

where A_0 is the activity of a sample of thickness X, A_E is the activity at infinite thickness, b is a constant having a value

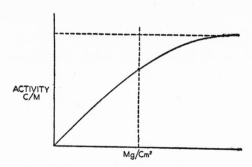

FIG. 9. Activity versus sample thickness.

of six, and R is the maximum range of the beta being measured as calculated from:

$$R = \frac{E^{5/3}}{150}$$

where E is the maximum energy in Kev. This equation may be expected to hold for energy values up to 200 Kev.

Correction may be made on samples, less than the infinite thickness, with the aid of correction factors. The correction factor C for a sample of given thickness is given by:

$$C = \frac{A_E}{A_0}$$

where A_E is the activity read from the extrapolated infinite thickness line and A_0 is the activity read from the plotted graph. In use, the activity and weight of an unknown sample are determined; then, from the previously constructed graph and the weight of the sample, the correction factor can be calculated. The observed activity is simply multiplied by the correction factor to obtain the true activity. Frequently to facilitate calculations, a graph of correction factors versus sample thickness is constructed.

APPARATUS AND MATERIALS

Geiger-Mueller Counter with a tube having a window thickness of two milligrams per square centimeter or less,

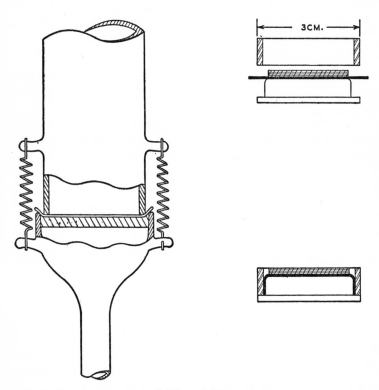

FIG. 10. Solid precipitate mounts.

precipitation apparatus (see Fig. 10), five 150-milliliter beakers, fifty milliliter burette, filter paper, rings and discs for precipitation apparatus (see Fig. 10), infrared lamp, 0.1 normal sulfuric acid containing two millicuries sulfur-35 per liter,[1] approximately 0.1 molar barium chloride solution, ninety-five per cent ethanol, acetone, sample holder.

PROCEDURE

An apparatus frequently used for the preparation of solid precipitates of low energy beta emitting substances is illustrated in Figure 10. A filter paper is placed over the fritted glass filter which is sealed onto the top of a pyrex cylinder. The paper is wetted thoroughly with water; the vacuum is turned on, and the glass tube is clamped in place by means of the springs which fit over the ears on the two pieces of the unit. Assemble this apparatus and prepare it in the manner described.

Measure from a burette into a 150 milliliter beaker exactly two milliliters of the radioactive sulfuric acid solution. Add to this an excess of barium chloride solution, and stir well to insure complete precipitation. Quantitatively transfer the solid barium sulfate to the filtration apparatus. Wash the precipitate thoroughly with ninety-five per cent ethanol and then with acetone, making certain that none of the material adheres to the tube wall. Carefully release the springs and remove the upper tube, then turn off the vacuum. Mount the precipitate by centering the filter paper on a brass disc and pressing on a brass ring to hold the paper securely as illustrated in Figure 10. The assembled unit is placed under an infrared lamp, and the precipitate is allowed to dry. After drying, the precipitate must be handled with extreme caution to prevent loss. The activity

[1] See Chapter IX.

of the precipitate is measured by placing the assembly in the sample holder under the Geiger-Mueller tube and counting for five minutes.

Repeat these operations using four, six, eight, and ten milliliters of the radioactive solution.

Calculations and Questions

1. From the normality of the sulfuric acid and the area of the precipitation apparatus tube calculate the milligrams per square centimeter for each of the samples.

2. Construct a graph plotting sample activities against sample thickness. Indicate the minimum infinite thickness.

3. Does the activity-thickness curve conform to the empirical equation given in the Theory section? Show calculations using this equation for three points on the curve.

4. Calculate the correction factors for ten points on the activity-thickness curve, and then make a plot of correction factors versus sample thicknesses.

Other Suggested Experiments

1. Measurement of betas from radioactive carbon in barium carbonate.

2. Measurement of calcium-45 in calcium carbonate.

References

R. H. Hendricks, L. C. Bryner, M. D. Thomas, and J. O. Ivie, *J. Phys. Chem.* 47, 469-473 (1943).

F. C. Henriques, Jr., G. B. Kistiakowsky, C. Margnetti, and W. G. Schneider, *Ind. Chem. Anal. Ed.* 18, 349 (1946).

M. D. Kamen, "Radioactive Tracers in Biology," Academic Press, Inc., New York, 1947, pp. 84-86.

W. F. Libby, *Anal. Chem.* 19, 2-6 (1947).

A. F. Reid, "Preparation and Measurement of Isotopic Tracers," J. W. Edwards, Ann Arbor, Michigan, 1947, 83-104.

P. E. Yankwich, T. H. Norris, and J. Huston, *Anal. Chem.* 19, 439-441 (1947).

VI. The Separation of Radioelements

OBJECT

Three methods for the separation of radioelements are illustrated in this experiment. The separation of uranium-X_1 from uranium is effected by nonaqueous solvent extraction and by ion exchange. An electrochemical separation is carried out using a radiumD-E-F mixture.

THEORY

Introduction. In the preparation of radioelements, it is frequently desirable to obtain the substance radioactively pure, that is, free from any other nuclear species. Due to the small concentrations of radioelements usually present, special methods have been devised and used for separations from gross amounts of inert substances. The most frequently used of these methods are coprecipitation (illustrated in the experiment on the Chemical Behavior of Micro-Quantities), electrochemical deposition, volatilization, nonaqueous extraction, ion exchange, and radioactive recoil (illustrated in the experiment on Separation of Nuclear Isomers). In this exercise, the methods of nonaqueous extraction and ion exchange will be illustrated by the extraction of uranium-X_1 from uranyl nitrate. Electrochemical deposition is used as a technique to separate radium-F and radium-E from radium-D.

Solvent Extraction. Nonaqueous solvent extractions are based upon the fact that certain compounds are more soluble in nonaqueous media than they are in water. The problem of quantitatively predicting which solute will be soluble in which solvent and to what extent is still an unsolved problem. A qualitative generalization that can be made is that polar solutes dissolve most readily in polar solvents and nonpolar materials in nonpolar solvents. Other factors entering in are hydrogen bonding, ionic-covalency relations, Werner complex formation, and polyacid character.

Ion Exchange. Ion exchange has been defined as the reversible interchange between a liquid phase and a solid body which does not involve any radical change in the structure of the solid. The solid substances used are of many types and are termed ion exchangers. These ion exchangers have either anions or cations that ionize in certain solvents and so may be replaced by other ions under certain conditions. They are classified according to cation or anion exchangers depending upon their function. The general exchange reaction for a cation exchanger may be given by the expression

$$E\,A + B^+ = E\,B + A^+$$

in which A and B are two cations competing for a position on the exchanger E.

Different ions attach themselves to the exchanger with various degrees of tenacity. By the use of a proper exchanger and proper solutions to remove the ions from the exchanger, separations may be effected. In actual practice a column is set up consisting of a glass tube the length and diameter of which may be varied within certain limits. This tube is filled with the exchanger which usually has as its exchangeable ion, in the case of cation exchangers, a sodium or hydrogen ion. The solution containing the cations in question is passed through the column and the cations are exchanged for the sodium or hydrogen ions in the exchanger. A specially prepared solution, termed the eluant, is then passed through the column. This solution will remove the ions in the inverse order of the degree of

firmness with which they are held. A separation may be
made by collecting the solution passing through the column
in several fractions. Frequently two or more eluants are
added in succession to disengage the desired ions. Many
factors enter into the thoroughness of separation, including
pH, relative complexing abilities, type of exchanger, rate
of flow of solutions through the column, density of the
exchanger bed, and other things. A
small experimental ion exchange apparatus is illustrated in Figure 11.

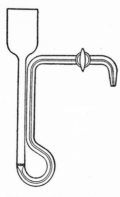

Properties of Uranium-X. In the
naturally occurring uranium-radium
series, the long-lived parent uranium-
238 decays through a series of
shorter-lived daughters finally ending
with a stable isotope of lead. These
daughter products vary greatly in
half-life and are present in their
secular equilibrium concentrations.
Some of these products are useful in
tracer work with the heavy elements,
the most important being uranium-X_1, the first decay
product in the series.

Fig. 11. Ion exchange
column.

Uranium-X_1 is an isotope of thorium with a mass number
of 234, decaying by beta emission to uranium-X_2 with a
half-life of twenty-four and five-tenths days. The ura-
nium-X_2 then decays by beta emission to uranium-234 with
a half-life of one and fourteen-hundredths minutes. The
beta particles from uranium-X_1 have a maximum energy
of only 0.13 Mev, and so they are not detected by the ordinary Geiger-Mueller Counter. The uranium-X_1, however,
establishes secular equilibrum with uranium-X_2 in less than
ten minutes and the beta particles from uranium-X_2 are
easily detected, the maximum energy being 2.32 Mev.

Electrochemical Deposition. Electrochemical methods are very important in the production of high specific activity radioactive materials. Substances may be selectively plated out on an electrode by keeping the potential of an electrolysis cell within certain values. On the other hand, the electrochemical character of various elements may be utilized, a more noble element plating out on a less noble one without the application of a current.

APPARATUS AND MATERIALS

Geiger-Mueller Counter, liquid counting apparatus, solid counting apparatus, an ion exchange column similar to that illustrated, Amberlite IR-100 exchanger resin, ethyl ether, ethyl acetate, 0.3 normal sulfuric acid, five per cent hydrochloric acid, radium-D-E-F solution 0.5 normal in hydrochloric acid,[1] one-inch squares of nickel and silver sheet or foil, one 50-milliliter beaker, three 150-milliliter beakers, separatory funnel, three 100-milliliter volumetric flasks, uranyl nitrate.

PROCEDURE

Solvent Extraction. Weigh out to 0.01 gram three five-gram portions of uranyl nitrate and place one sample in each of three beakers. Add to one beaker exactly fifty milliliters of water, to another fifty milliliters of ethyl ether and five milliliters of water, and to the third fifty milliliters of ethyl acetate and five milliliters of water. Stir the mixtures thoroughly. Pour the solution in the first beaker into a 100-milliliter volumetric flask and dilute with water to the mark. Transfer the mixture from the second beaker to a separatory funnel and drain the water off into another volumetric flask. Dilute this to the mark with

[1] See Chapter IX.

water. Repeat the procedure on the third mixture. After
making sure that the solution is thoroughly mixed, fill the
liquid counting apparatus to the mark from the first
volumetric flask and measure its activity. Discard the
solution, wash the liquid counting apparatus three times
with tapwater, twice with distilled water; rinse it out with
acetone, and dry by passing a stream of air through it.
Repeat the activity measurement on the second and third
samples. Recover the uranyl nitrate by evaporation of the
solutions.

Ion Exchange.[2] Introduce the exchanger resin into an
ion exchange column similar to that shown in Fig. 11 by
pouring a suspension of the completely wet resin in water
into the opened top of the tube. Open the outlet stopcock
and allow the resin to settle slowly to form a bed. Add
enough resin so that a column thirteen to fifteen centimeters
long is produced.

Weigh out to 0.01 gram a ten-gram portion of uranyl
nitrate and dissolve it in about 100 milliliters of water.
Close the column stopcock and pour the uranium solution
into the funnel. Adjust the stopcock to allow the solution
to flow through at the rate of about two drops per second.
When this solution has run through the column, add 100
milliliters of water and allow it to run through at a rate
of five drops per second. Discard the solutions from these
two runs.

Pour through the column at the rate of five drops per
second 200 milliliters of 0.3 normal sulfuric acid followed
by 100 milliliters of water. Discard these solutions. Then
add to the column 400 milliliters of five per cent hydrochloric acid; drain off fifty milliliters at the rate of five
drops per second, then collect in three 100 milliliter
volumetric flasks three 100 milliliter portions of the solu-

[2] See Chapter IX.

tion coming through the column. Using the liquid counting apparatus measure the activities of each of these solutions.

Electrochemical Separations. Place about 40 milliliters of the prepared radium-D (lead)-radium-E (bismuth)-radium-F (polonium) solution in a 50-milliliter beaker. Polish a square of silver sheet and one of nickel sheet to a high luster with emery cloth. Rotate the silver sheet in the solution for one and one-half to two hours. Wash the sheet with water, then with acetone, and allow it to dry. Turn this sheet of silver in to the instructor, who will use it to demonstrate an alpha counter.

Heat the remaining solution to 80 degrees Centigrade on a steam bath, and rotate the nickel sheet in it for 30 minutes. Remove the metal, wash as previously, and prepare a mount designed to count one surface of it. Run a beta count on the sample and repeat this counting procedure once every two days for the next two weeks.

Calculations and Questions

1. Calculate the per cent of uranium-X_1 removed by the extractions with ethyl ether and ethyl acetate.

2. Calculate the per cent of uranium-X_1 removed by each fraction in the ion exchange process.

3. The half-life of uranium-238 is 4.5×10^9 years, that of uranium-X_1 is 24.5 days, and that of uranium-X_2 is 1.14 minutes. Calculate the amounts of uranium-X_1 and uranium-X_2 in equilibrium with a one gram sample of uranium-238.

4. One gram of uranium-238 emits 1.15×10^4 alpha particles per second. How many beta particles does the equilibrium amount of uranium-X_2 emit per second?

5. A certain sample of uranium-X_1 emits 1,000 beta particles per second.

(a) How many particles will be emitted per second fifteen days later? (b) How many grams are there in a curie of uranium-X_1?

(c) How many grams are in the sample above? (d) How many atoms will be present after fifteen days? (e) How long will it take the activity to decay to 0.1 per cent of its initial value?

6. Describe what is taking place in the electrochemical separation, and list the five metals involved in their order of apparent nobility.

7. Calculate the half-life of the beta-emitter separated on the nickel. Identify it.

Other Suggested Experiments

1. Ion exchange separations of the rare earths.
2. Extraction of Gallium from Zinc.

References

G. Hevesy and F. A. Paneth, "A Manual of Radioactivity," Oxford University Press, London, 1938, pp. 126-132, 215-223.

O. Hahn, "Applied Radiochemistry," Cornell University Press, Ithaca, New York, 1936, pp. 23-48.

E. Rutherford, J. Chadwick, and C. D. Ellis, "Radiations from Radioactive Substances," The Macmillan Co., New York, 1930, pp. 551-562.

M. D. Kamen, "Radioactive Tracers in Biology," Academic Press, Inc., New York, 1947, pp. 36-41.

R. Moore and H. Schlundt, *Phil. Mag.* 12, 393-396 (1907).

W. E. Cohn, George W. Parker, and E. R. Tompkins, *Nucleonics* 3, No. 5, 22 (1948).

O. Erbacher and K. Phillipp, *Z. physik.* 51, 309-320 (1928).

VII.   The Chemical Behavior of Micro-Quantities

OBJECT

This experiment is designed to illustrate some of the behaviorisms of extremely dilute solutions, as are often encountered in work with radioactive materials. Both adsorption and coprecipitation phenomena are studied.

THEORY

Introduction. The behavior of micro-quantities of radioelements in adsorption and precipitation processes is quite important, since these phenomena provide methods for separation. In addition, the two mechanisms are frequently more a source of trouble than they are an aid. For these reasons it is necessary that the processes be recognized and controlled in work with very dilute solutions of radioactive materials.

Various experiments have shown that under certain circumstances, radioelements exist in colloidal form in solutions of extreme dilution. These colloidal aggregates can be centrifuged; they are adsorbed by filter paper, membranes, and other substances presenting sizable surface area, and they frequently deposit on the surfaces of glass apparatus. Addition of ions of the opposite charge to the radiocolloidal aggregates seems to cause the particles to break up and go into true solution.

Adsorption. Surface adsorption is the coprecipitation of an element on the active surface of a freshly preformed precipitate. The amount of adsorption depends primarily upon the charge of the precipitate and the solubility of compounds formed from the ion that is coprecipitated and the ions in the precipitate. Other factors such as temperature, the order of addition of reagents, the speed of precipitate formation, and digestion processes also may affect the adsorption, but the precipitate charge and insolubility relations are the most important.

In the precipitate AX, if an excess of X^- or OH^- is present, the surface will be negatively charged due to the adsorption of these anions, and positive ions in solution will attach themselves to those negatively charged adsorbed ions and be coprecipitated. Conversely, if an excess of

A^+ or H^+ is present, the precipitate will be positively charged due to an adsorption of these ions. In this instance, negative ions present in the solution will attach themselves and be carried down. It has also been shown that those ions whose compounds with the oppositely charged constituent of the precipitate are slightly soluble in the solvent used are well adsorbed by the precipitate.

Isomorphous Replacement. The replacement of a structural unit in a crystal by some other unit of similar size without distortion of the crystal structure is termed isomorphous replacement. In most instances, the units are ions and the crystals are those that are precipitated from solutions. Such a replacement process would lead to a uniform distribution of a low concentration radioactive substance in the crystals of a high concentration substance when the two materials are crystallized or precipitated together. This principle is the basis of the widely used carrier method for the separation of radioisotopes from each other and from inert materials. A quantity of stable material, chemically identical or similar to the desired radioisotope, is added to a minute quantity of a radioelement in solution with several other active or stable elements. The usual chemical precipitations are then carried out. The radioactive substance follows the carrier in the separation.

The amount of carrying is almost independent of the temperature, acidity, and order of addition of reagents, but depends to a great extent upon the chemical similarity of the coprecipitated ion and the like-charged ion in the precipitate.

Other Phenomena. Anomalous isomorphous replacement is a phenomenon similar to isomorphous replacement except that it is not observed in microscopic amounts of the two materials. The amount of radioactive substance so precipitated in this fashion approaches maximum and is independent of the method of precipitation. It has been suggested that a very narrow range of solid solution of the compound of the radioelement in the compound of the carrier element exists.

Frequently internal adsorption is found. This is usually a result of fast crystallization in which some of the mother liquor is mechanically enclosed within the crystal. The amount of coprecipitated substance obviously depends upon a great many factors.

APPARATUS AND MATERIALS

Geiger-Mueller Counter, liquid counting apparatus, centrifuge, two five-milliliter centrifuge tubes, fifty milliliter burette, seven 100-milliliter volumetric flasks, ten 150-milliliter beakers, six funnels, funnel rack, filter paper, aluminum foil, rough balance, infrared lamp, stop watch, one 300-milliliter beaker, 0.1-milliliter pipette, cardboard mounting cards, cellophane, Scotch tape.

Uranyl nitrate, ferric nitrate solution five grams per liter, five per cent sodium bicarbonate solution, 0.1 normal silver nitrate solution, sodium iodate solution twenty grams per liter, sodium fluoride solution eighty grams per liter, cerium chloride solution twenty-five grams per liter, thorium chloride solution twenty-seven grams per liter, dilute (six normal) sulfuric acid, acetone.

PROCEDURE

Adsorption Phenomena. Weigh out approximately forty grams of hydrated uranyl nitrate. Dissolve this material in about 250 milliliters of water and deliver exactly twenty-five milliliters of this prepared solution from a burette into each of five 100-milliliter volumetric flasks. Then place exactly ten milliliters of the silver nitrate solution in each of four 150-milliliter beakers and precipitate all of the silver by addition of an excess of sodium iodate solution. Wash each precipitate thoroughly and filter. Punch a hole in each filter paper and wash one of the precipitates into each of four of the volumetric flasks containing the uranyl nitrate solution. To one of the flasks containing a precipitate add about ten milliliters of the sodium iodate solution to another ten milliliters of the silver nitrate solution, and to a third five drops of dilute (six normal) sulfuric acid. Make all five of the volumetric flasks up to the mark with water and allow to stand with frequent shakings for about fifteen minutes. Filter each solution and collect the filtrate in 150 milliliter beakers. Transfer a sufficient volume of one of the filtrates to the liquid counting apparatus to fill to the mark and measure its activity. Discard the solution, wash the liquid counting apparatus three times with tap water, then twice with distilled water, rinse it out with acetone, and dry by passing a stream of air through it. Repeat this measurement procedure for each filtrate.

Separation of Radioelements by Adsorption. Deliver into a 150-milliliter beaker one milliliter of the prepared uranyl nitrate solution. Add to this one milliliter of the ferric nitrate solution and fifteen milliliters of the sodium bicarbonate solution. Warm the mixture gently on a hotplate until the ferric hydroxide coagulates. Allow to cool, transfer a portion of the slurry to a five-milliliter centrifuge cone, and centrifuge for about two minutes. Remove the supernatent liquid being careful not to disturb the precipitate. Carefully add another portion of the slurry and repeat the centrifuging and liquid removal processes. Continue this procedure until all the precipitate has been transferred to the cone. Rinse the beaker twice with approximately 0.5 milliliter water and treat in the same manner as the slurry, then wash the precipitate twice with one milliliter water, discarding the supernatent liquid each time. Suspend the precipitate in 0.1 milliliter of water and with the 0.1 milliliter pipette transfer it to a piece of aluminum foil. Dry under the infrared lamp, mount on a card, cover with cellophane, and fasten securely with Scotch tape. Determine the activity of the sample. Set the sample aside and determine its activity once a week for the following two weeks.

Isomorphous Replacement. Into each of two 100-milliliter volumetric flasks, deliver from a burette exactly twenty-five milliliters of the prepared uranyl nitrate solution. Then add ten milliliters of the cerium chloride solution to one, and ten milliliters of the thorium chloride to the other. Add fifty milliliters of water and ten milliliters of the sodium fluoride solution to each, followed by dilution with water to the mark. Allow the flasks to stand with frequent shakings for about fifteen minutes. Filter the samples collecting the filtrates in 150 milliliter beakers. Determine the activity of each of these solutions by measurement in the liquid counting apparatus.

Calculations and Questions

1. Calculate the percentage activity coprecipitated by each of the following carrier substances:

(a) Silver iodate. (b) Silver iodate in excess iodate ion. (c) Silver iodate in excess silver ion. (d) Silver iodate in excess hydrogen ion. (e) Cerous fluoride. (f) Thorium flouride.

2. Explain the differences in coprecipitation phenomena as observed above.

3. Plot the activity of the ferric oxide absorbed uranium-X_1 as a

function of time in days on semi-log graph paper and determine the half-life.

Other Suggested Experiments

1. Behavior of thorium B (lead) with barium chloride crystals.
2. Retention of yttrium on filter paper.
3. Behavior of thorium B (lead) and thorium C (bismuth) in various electrolytes.

References

O. Hahn, "Applied Radiochemistry," Cornell University Press, Ithaca, New York, 1936, pp. 50-164.

J. D. Kurbatov and Kurbatov, *J. Phys. Chem.* **46**, 441 (1942).

A. Werner, *Z. physik Chem.* **A 156**, 89 (1939).

G. Hevesy and F. A. Paneth, "A Manual of Radioactivity," Oxford University Press, London, 1938, pp. 126-128, 161-165.

CHAPTER VI

CHEMICAL EXPERIMENTS

VIII. SOLUBILITY DETERMINATIONS

OBJECT

The ease and accuracy with which solubility experiments may be made utilizing radioisotopes are illustrated in this experiment. The solubilities of several compounds of strontium are measured.

THEORY

Many solubilities have been determined with the aid of radioisotopes. The accuracy of the measurements can be made very reliable by altering the specific activity of the substance whose solubility is to be determined.

In practice a definite amount of the almost insoluble compound is prepared containing a known amount of radioactivity. This substance is placed with a solvent and agitated at constant temperature until equilibrium has been reached. The radioactivity of the solution is then measured, and the fraction of the activity present indicates the fraction of material dissolved.

APPARATUS AND MATERIALS

Geiger-Mueller Counter, liquid counting apparatus, holder, 0.1 molar strontium nitrate solution containing two millicuries of radioactive strontium per liter,[1] solutions ap-

[1] See Chapter IX.

proximately 0.1 molar of sodium sulfate, ammonium carbonate, and oxalic acid; solution of sodium fluoride approximately 0.1 molar, four 140-milliliter wide-mouthed bottles with screw-on caps, one fifty-milliliter volumetric flask, four funnels, filter paper, four fifty-milliliter beakers, one five-milliliter pipette, one 0.1-milliliter pipette, shaker or constant-temperature water bath.

PROCEDURE

Place in each of four beakers about five milliliters of the radioactive strontium nitrate solution. Add to one a slight excess of approximately 0.1 molar oxalic acid, to another sodium sulfate solution, to another sodium fluoride solution, and to the last ammonium carbonate solution. Only slight excesses of these solutions should be added, since large excesses exert a strong solvent action on the precipitated strontium compounds. Filter and thoroughly wash each of these precipitates, discarding the filtrates. After perforating the filter papers, wash each precipitate into a 140-milliliter wide-mouthed bottle. Add enough extra water to bring the volume of each up to approximately fifty to sixty milliliters. Close the bottles and place them in a mechanical shaker or a constant-temperature water bath having a revolving sample holder.

Allow the samples to be agitated for as long as the laboratory period will allow. Remove the bottles and filter off the precipitates, collecting the filtrates in 150-milliliter beakers. Measure the activities of each of the filtrates in the liquid counting apparatus.

Pipette 0.1 milliliter of the radiostrontium solution into a fifty-milliliter volumetric flask, dilute to the mark, and mix well. Measure the activity of this solution in the liquid counting apparatus.

Calculations and Questions

1. Justify the comparison of the activities of the samples and the standard, even though the total volume in the samples was not critical.

2. Calculate the solubilities of each of the strontium compounds. Compare these with the values obtained from the literature. Account for any major differences.

Other Suggested Experiments

1. Solubility of various phosphates using phosphorus-32.
2. Solubility of silver compounds using silver-111.
3. Solubility of thorium compounds using uranium-X.

References

B. N. Cacciapuoti and E. Ferla, *Ann. Chim. Applicata* 29, 166 (1939) ; *C. A.* 33, 9091 (1939).

M. Ishibashi and H. Kishi, *Bull. Chem. Soc. Japan* 10, 362 (1935).

G. Hevesy and F. Paneth, *Z. anorg. Chem.* 82, 322 (1913).

G. Hevesy and E. Roma, *Z. physik Chem.* 89, 294, 303 (1915).

IX. Exchange reactions (Precipitate-Ion)

OBJECT

The use of radioactive indicators in exchange investigations will be illustrated in this experiment. The exchange of silver between precipitated silver chloride and silver ions in solution is studied in relation to time and variations in concentration.

THEORY

A reaction involving exchange corresponding to the equation

$$AB + B' = AB' + B$$

can be detected only if the chemically identical atoms B and B' can be distinguished. An important method that is available is the use of radioactive isotopes of the element B. Exchange reactions involving radioisotopes have been shown to be of the first order. Therefore, it is possible to measure half-life values of equilibrium reactions as indications of the rapidity of exchange.

Many exchange experiments have been carried out using radioactive materials. These experiments have yielded much information about bond strengths, structures, mechanisms, surface phenomena, and kinetics. In practice, atoms of the element to be investigated are "labeled" with radioatoms in the same chemical form. The labeled substance is then mixed with an unlabeled substance of the same element but in a different state of chemical combination. The materials are allowed to remain in contact with each other for a definite period of time. This is followed by a determination of the activity transferred to the originally inactive form. The most common types of exchange are atom-ion, precipitate-ion, and ion-ion reactions.

Complete exchange is evidenced when the radioactivity becomes distributed between the two chemical forms in the same ratio as the amounts of the exchanging element in the two forms. If A_I is the initial specific activity of the active chemical form, A_E its specific activity observed after equilibrium has been attained with the nonactive form, and A_T the specific activity after time T has elapsed, then the per cent completeness of the exchange ϵ at time T is given by

$$\epsilon = \frac{A_I - A_T}{A_I - A_E} \cdot 100$$

Frequently in precipitate-ion exchanges and atom-ion exchanges only the surface atoms on a solid in contact with the ion will exchange with the active solution. This permits the determination of the weight of exchangeable substance on the solid material by use of the following proportion

$$\frac{M_{surf}}{M_{soln}} = \frac{A_I - A_E}{A_E}$$

where M_{surf} is the weight of the exchangeable material on the solid's surface, M_{soln} its weight in the solution, and A_I and A_E are as previously used. The weight of the substance M_{surf} is divided by its atomic weight (W_{at}) and multiplied by the Avogadro number to find the total number of atoms (N) on the surface, or

$$N = \frac{M_{surf}}{W_{at}} \cdot 6.02 \times 10^{23}$$

The area of the surface may then be expressed in square centimeters by multiplying the number of atoms by the cross section of the atom or molecule making up the solid. The cross-sectional values can usually be obtained from crystallographic data.

In some cases all the atoms in a solid will undergo exchange. This is generally attributed to intracrystal diffusion processes. If all the atoms in a solid were undergoing exchange with an ion in solution, then a homogeneous distribution of the radioactive material throughout the whole system would be evidenced. Such a system conforms to the following equation

$$A_E = A_I \frac{M_{soln}}{M_{tot}}$$

in which A_E, A_I, and M_{soln} retain their previous significance and M_{tot} is the total amount of the exchanging substance in the system, or

$$M_{tot} = M_{soln} + M_{solid}$$

where M_{solid} is the amount of the exchanging substance in the solid.

In many cases solids may exhibit phenomena intermediate between the two extremes of surface adsorption and complete exchange. The degree of this is dependent upon concentration, rate of precipitation, particle size, agitation, and several other factors.

APPARATUS AND MATERIALS

Geiger-Mueller Counter, open solution or dipping counter apparatus, 0.1 normal silver nitrate solution, 0.1 normal silver nitrate solution containing one to two millicuries of radioactive silver per liter,[1] approximately 0.1 normal sodium chloride solution, dilute nitric acid, six funnels and filter paper to fit, seven fifty-milliliter volumetric flasks, stop watch, shaker or water bath, six 200-milliliter glass-stoppered wide-mouthed bottles, one five-milliliter pipette and syringe, six 150-milliliter beakers, twenty-five-milliliter burette and stand.

PROCEDURE

Into each of seven fifty-milliliter volumetric flasks, pipette five milliliters of the radioactive silver nitrate solution. Into each of four 150-milliliter beakers introduce five milliliters of the non-active silver nitrate solution from the burette, into a fifth beaker 1.5 milliliters, and into a sixth 8.5 milliliters. Add to each of these beakers ten drops of dilute nitric acid and an excess of the sodium chloride solution. Stir well, filter, and wash the precipitates, discarding the filtrates. After puncturing the filter papers, wash one of these precipitates into each of six of the volumetric flasks

[1] See Chapter IX.

containing the radioactive solution. Dilute all seven volumetric flasks to the mark with water and shake well. Start the stop watch. Transfer the solutions and precipitates in each of the six flasks containing them to small glass-stoppered wide-mouthed bottles having volumes of about 200 milliliters. Do not add any more liquid. Stopper the bottles and place them in a shaking machine or a constant-temperature bath containing an agitation apparatus. Using the liquid counting apparatus, measure the activity of the solution containing no precipitate.

After a lapse of twenty minutes, filter one of the solutions containing a precipitate produced from five milliliters of nonactive silver nitrate solution. Collect the filtrate in a 150-milliliter beaker and measure the activity of a portion of it in the liquid counting apparatus. Measure the activities of the three remaining five-milliliter precipitate samples after the lapse of thirty, seventy, and one hundred and ten minutes.

Measure the activities of the filtrates of the other two samples after the lapse of 120 minutes.

Calculations and Questions

1. Construct a graph plotting the counts per minute of the solution against the time of contact with the precipitate for the precipitates of equal weight.

2. Calculate the per cent completeness of exchange for each of the time periods.

3. Explain your conclusions.

4. From the data on the precipitates of unequal weight, determine whether all of the precipitate atoms are undergoing exchange.

5. Calculate the standard deviation for each determination.

6. Briefly outline an exchange that has not been performed.

Other Suggested Experiments

1. Exchange between lead chloride and plumbous ion with radioactive lead.

2. Exchange between thallous ion and thallic ion with radioactive thallium.

3. Exchange between methyl iodide and iodide ion with radioactive iodine.

References

G. T. Seaborg, *Chem. Reviews* **27**, 260-70 (1940).

A. Langer, *J. Chem. Phys.* **10**, 321-7 (1942).

W. A. Koehler and J. H. Mathews, *J. Am. Chem. Soc.* **46**, 1158 (1924).

O. Hahn, "Applied Radiochemistry," Cornell University Press, Ithaca, New York, 1936, pp. 172-186.

F. Paneth, "Radioelements as Indicators," McGraw-Hill Book Co., Inc., New York, 1928, pp. 55-79.

G. Hevesy and L. Zeichmeister, *Ber.* **53B**, 410 (1920); *C. A.* **14**, 2932 (1920).

H. A. C. McKay, *Nature* **139**, 238 (1937).

F. Juliusberger, B. Topley, and J. Weiss, *J. Chem. Phys.* **3**, 437 (1935).

G. Hevesy and M. Blitz, *Z. physik Chem.* **B3**, 271 (1929).

J. Zirkler, *Z. physik Chem.* **A187**, 103 (1940); *J. Am. Chem. Soc.* **70**, 880 (1948).

X. EXCHANGE REACTIONS (ATOM-ION)

OBJECT

This experiment is intended to show the method for investigations of exchange reactions between a metal and ions in solution using radioactive indicators.

THEORY

See the previous experiment for the theory relating to this type of exchange.

APPARATUS AND MATERIALS

Zinc bar 1 × 5 × 7.5 centimeters, 0.01-molar solution of zinc nitrate containing one millicurie of radioactive zinc per liter,[1] 100-milliliter beaker, Geiger-Mueller Counter, crocus cloth.

PROCEDURE

Polish the zinc bar to a high lustre with crocus cloth. Suspend it in fifty milliliters of the active zinc nitrate solution. Every fifteen minutes, remove the strip, wash it thoroughly, dry it, and measure its activity. Continue this procedure for six fifteen-minute periods.

Calculations and Questions

1. Construct a graph plotting activity against time elapsed.

2. Assuming the activity of the solution to be exactly one microcurie per milliliter, the counter efficiency ten per cent, and the self-absorption zero, calculate the number of atomic layers of the metal that have taken place in the exchange after each time period.

Other Suggested Experiments

1. Exchange of silver and silver ion.
2. Exchange of sulfur and carbon disulfide.
3. Exchange of lead and plumbous ion.

References

B. V.Rollin, *J. Am. Chem. Soc.* **62**, 86 (1940).
G. G. Jons, *J. Chem. Phys.* **9**, 775 (1941).

[1] See Chapter IX.

R. A. Cooley, D. M. Yost, and E. McMillan, *J. Am. Chem. Soc.*
61, 2970 (1939).

G. von Hevesy and M. Blitz, *Z. physik Chem.* B3, 271 (1929).

XI. Exchange Reactions (Ion-Ion)

OBJECT

The utility of exchange reactions in structural inorganic chemistry is demonstrated in this exercise. Carbon-14 is used to label the oxalate ion and to follow its exchange with the oxalate-complexes of iron and chromium.

THEORY

Many trivalent metal ions form oxalate complexes with the alkali metal oxalates. They have the general formula:

$$A_3M(C_2O_4)_3$$

in which A is the alkali metal and M is the trivalent metal. Pauling has shown that the bonds between the trivalent metal and the oxalate ions may be ionic or covalent. If the trivalent metal ion supplies two d, three p, and one s orbital, for bonding, then, provided that certain other conditions are met, the configuration of the complex will be octahedral.

Let us take the ferric ion as an example. If the bonding is covalent, the oxalate complex will have the following electronic structure:

$$\begin{array}{cccccc} & 3s & 3p & 3d & 4s & 4p \\ Fe(C_2O_4)_3{}^{---}: & ::: & ::.:: & : & ::: \end{array}$$

the twelve extra electrons being contributed by the three oxalate ions. This configuration would theoretically give a magnetic moment value of 1.76 corresponding to the presence of one unpaired electron. On the other hand, if the ferric-oxalate bonds were ionic, the oxalate ions would not contribute their twelve electrons to the structure, and the central ion would have a structure:

$$\text{Fe}^{+++}: \quad \begin{array}{cccc} 3s & 3p & 3d & 4s \\ :: & ::: & ..... & \end{array}$$

This would show a theoretical magnetic moment of 5.92, corresponding to five unpaired electrons. Magnetic measurements show that the moment of this complex is 5.9, indicating an ionic structure. If such a conclusion is true, then oxalate ions in solution should exchange readily with the ions in the complex.

Similar considerations may be applied to other trivalent ions.

APPARATUS AND MATERIALS

Geiger-Mueller Counter, ten-milliliter pipette, three twenty-five milliliter graduates, three 100-milliliter beakers, seventy-five milliliters of 0.05-molar radioactive potassium oxalate solution,[1] twenty-five milliliters of 0.05-molar potassium trioxalato-chromate(III) solution,[2] twenty-five milliliters of 0.05-molar potassium trioxalatoferrate(III) solution,[2] approximately 0.05-molar calcium chloride solution.

PROCEDURE

Mix in a 100-milliliter beaker twenty-five-milliliter portions of the radioactive potassium oxalate solution and the potassium trioxalatochromate(III). Repeat this procedure, using the iron complex in place of the chromium one. Allow these mixtures to stand for one hour. In the meantime, transfer another twenty-five-milliliter portion of the radioactive oxalate solution to a 100-milliliter beaker. Add to this exactly ten milliliters of the calcium chloride solution.

[1] See Chapter IX.

Using the procedure as outlined in Experiment V, measure the activity of the precipitate.

To each of the exchange mixtures add exactly ten milliliters of the calcium chloride solution, and measure the activities of the precipitates.

Calculations and Questions

1. Indicate the precipitates that exchanged.

2. Explain the exchange or nonexchange of each material, and relate this to magnetic measurements and electronic configurations.

3. Suggest ways in which this experiment could be made quantitative.

4. Why was not all of the oxalate precipitated from the reaction mixtures?

5. Why is no correction for self-absorption necessary?

Other Suggested Experiments

1. Exchange of trioxalatoaluminate ion and trioxalatocobaltate (III) ions with oxalate ions.

2. Exchange of hexacyanocobaltate (III) ion and hexacyano chromate (III) ion with cyanide ions.

3. Exchange of sulfite and sulfate ions.

References

F. A. Long, *J. Am. Chem. Soc.* **61**, 570 (1939).

Ibid. **63**, 1353 (1941).

L. Pauling, "The Nature of the Chemical Bond," Cornell University Press, Ithaca, New York, 1939, pp. 112.

H. H. Voge, *J. Am. Chem. Soc.* **61**, 1032 (1939).

J. F. Flagg, *J. Am. Chem. Soc.* **63**, 557 (1941).

R. B. Duffield and M. Calvin, *J. Am. Chem. Soc.* **68**, 557 (1946).

XII. Quantitative Analysis with a Radioindicator

OBJECT

The purpose of this experiment is to illustrate the use of radioisotopes as an analytical tool. The concentration of silver in an unknown solution is determined by the precipitation of silver phosphate containing radioactive phosphorus.

THEORY

Anions and cations may be precipitated by the addition of certain reagents. If the reagent contains radioactive atoms which are precipitated, then this gives an excellent method for quantitative analysis of the desired anion or cation.

In this exercise, silver is precipitated as silver phosphate by the addition of an excess of a standard phosphate solution containing radiophosphorus. The precipitate is buffered to insure quantitative removal. The precipitate is filtered out, and the phosphate remaining in the solution is determined by measuring the activity of the filtrate. As in any analytical procedure where an excess of reagent is determined, the accuracy of the method is enhanced by only a slight excess.

APPARATUS AND MATERIALS

Geiger-Mueller Counter, liquid counting apparatus, holder, 0.01-molar standard disodium phosphate solution containing one millicurie of radioactive phosphorus per liter,[1] approximately 0.03-molar silver nitrate solution, three 100-milliliter volumetric flasks, five per cent sodium

[1] See Chapter IX.

bicarbonate solution, three funnels, filter paper, three 150-milliliter beakers, two burettes.

PROCEDURE

Deliver exactly twenty milliliters of the silver nitrate solution into each of three 100-milliliter volumetric flasks. Add slowly to one flask, with stirring, twenty-three milliliters of the standard phosphate solution, followed by four milliliters of five-per-cent sodium bicarbonate solution. Stir well. Dilute to the mark with water, and warm the flask on a steam bath for a few minutes. Allow the flask to cool, and then filter off the precipitate, collecting the filtrate in a 150-milliliter beaker. Fill the liquid counting apparatus, and measure the activity of a portion of this solution. Repeat the procedure for the two other samples.

Into a 100-milliliter volumetric flask, place two milliliters of the standard radiophosphorus solution. Dilute to the mark, mix thoroughly, and measure the activity on the liquid counting apparatus.

Calculations and Questions

1. Calculate the molarity of the silver solution as measured in each of the three determinations. Average the three results.

2. Devise a formula for the calculation of the molarity of the silver solution and another for milligrams of silver per milliliter.

3. What major source of error is present in the method as outlined here? How could this be corrected?

Other Suggested Experiments

1. Determination of zinc ion as the phosphate with radioactive phosphorus.

2. Determination of silver ion as the iodide with radioactive iodine.

3. Determination of sulfate ion as the strontium salt with radioactive strontium.

4. Determination of chloride ion as the silver salt with radioactive silver.

5. Use an end window Geiger-Mueller tube with prepared mounts in any of the above experiments.

References

A. Langer, *J. Phys. Chem.* **45,** 639 (1941).

Henri Moreau, Paul Chavin, and Raymond Daudel, *Compt. Rend.* **219,** 127 (1944).

P. Sue, *Bull. Soc. Chim.* **1946,** 102; *C. A.* **40,** 5659 (1946).

J. F. Flagg and E. O. Wiig, *Ind. Eng. Chem. Anal. Ed.* **13,** 341 (1941).

XIII. Analysis by Isotopic Dilution

OBJECT

Quantitative analysis by the radioisotopic dilution method is illustrated in this exercise. The amount of iron in several unknown solutions is determined.

THEORY

The isotopic dilution method of analysis consists of a simple set of successive operations. An isotopically labeled compound is added to an unknown mixture. This is allowed to come to equilibrium, and then the same compound is isolated from the system. The isotopic content of the original compound is then compared with that of the final one. The ratio of the two specific activities depends on the relative amounts of the substance added and that already present.

A very important advantage of this method is that a

quantitative isolation of the final material is not at all necessary. Only a sample large enough to give accurate weight determinations is required; this sample should weigh at least twenty milligrams.

An amount of substance weighing G_1 milligrams having an activity A_1 will have a specific activity S_1 given by the relation:

$$S_1 = \frac{A_1}{G_1}$$

If this material is added to G_2 milligrams of inactive substance, then the final specific activity S_F will be:

$$S_F = \frac{A_1}{G_1 + G_2}$$

Solving these two equations for the unknown weight G_2, we obtain

$$G_2 = G_1 \left(\frac{S_1}{S_F} - 1 \right)$$

The error caused by neglecting the differences in molecular weight of the radioactive and stable isotopes is very small and can be assumed zero in almost all cases.

APPARATUS AND MATERIALS

Geiger-Mueller Counter, solution about 0.1 molar ferric chloride containing five millicuries radioactive iron per liter,[1] unknown ferric chloride solution between 0.1 molar and 0.5 molar, sodium chloride, cobaltous chloride, ethyl ether, eight normal hydrochloric acid, eight two-inch watch glasses, three 150-milliliter beakers, a one-milliliter pipette, a two-milliliter pipette, three 100-milliliter separatory funnels, infra-red lamp.

[1] See Chapter IX.

PROCEDURE

Place in each of three beakers exactly ten milliliters of the unknown ferric chloride solution. Add to each exactly one milliliter of the radio-iron solution, and stir well. Then add to one beaker about fifty milligrams of sodium chloride and to another fifty milligrams sodium chloride and fifty milligrams cobaltous chloride. Stir both until the solids are dissolved. Remove from one of the beakers about two milliliters of the solution, and place in a small separatory funnel. Pour into the separatory funnel about five milliliters of ethyl ether and five milliliters of eight normal hydrochloric acid. Stopper and shake well. Allow the layers to settle, and then drain off the ether layer onto a watch glass. Evaporate the ether off under an infrared lamp. Immediately weigh the sample to the fourth place, and determine its activity. Repeat the procedure, using each of the other two samples and then using exactly two milliliters of the radio-iron solution.

Calculations and Questions

1. In each case, calculate the milligrams of iron present in the unknown solution, assuming that, for the radio-iron solution, the partition coefficient was twenty-eight.

2. Calculate the normality of the unknown iron solution from the average of the values obtained in question 1.

3. Derive an equation which includes a correction for the weight difference of the added isotope and the diluent isotope.

References

D. C. Graham and G. T. Seaborg, *J. Am. Chem. Soc.* **60**, 2524 (1938).

M. D. Kamen, "Radioactive Tracers in Biology," Academic Press, New York, 1947, pp. 112-118.

N. S. Radin, *Nucleonics* **1**, No. 2, 49 (1947).

G. Hevesy and E. Hofer, *Nature* **134**, 879 (1934).

D. Rittenberg and G. L. Foster, *J. Biol. Chem.* **133**, 737 (1940).

H. H. Ussing, *Nature* **144**, 977 (1939).

P. Sue, *Nature* **157**, 622 (1946).

XIV. Transference Numbers

OBJECT

This experiment is intended to demonstrate the determination of transference numbers, using radioisotopic analysis. The transference number of silver in silver nitrate is determined, using radioactive silver as an analytical tool.

THEORY

The transference number of an ion may be defined as the fraction of the total current which it carries during the process of electrolysis. During electrolysis, concentration changes take place around the electrodes and these changes serve as a measure of the ionic velocities. Consider a tube about twelve inches long, having an electrode at each end and a stopcock in the middle filled with a solution containing the ion whose transference number is desired. The stopcock is opened, and a known amount of electricity is passed through the solution for a definite length of time. The stopcock is then closed, and the separate solutions in the two compartments are analyzed.

The transference numbers of the ions may be determined from the following formulas:

$$t_c = \frac{\Delta_c}{e}$$

$$t_a = \frac{\Delta_a}{e}$$

where t_c = the transference number of the cation

t_a = the transference number of the anion

Δ_c = the reduction in equivalents of cation in the anode compartment due to migration

Δ_a = the reduction in equivalents of anion in the cathode compartment due to migration

e = the number of equivalents of electricity passed through the solution during electrolysis.

In this experiment it is assumed that the differences in velocities of the three silver ions—silver-107, silver-108, and silver-111—are negligible even though their masses differ.

APPARATUS AND MATERIALS

Geiger-Mueller Counter, open solution or dipping counter apparatus, holder, 0.1 normal silver nitrate containing thirty-five to fifty microcuries of radiosilver per liter,[1] dilute hydrochloric acid, transference number cell,[1] two 100-milliliter beakers, silver or copper coulometer, milliammeter, rheostat, source of d-c current, connecting wire, stop watch.

PROCEDURE

The apparatus to be used in this experiment is illustrated in Figure 12. The volumes of the compartments, which should be approximately thirty-five milliliters each, will be furnished by the instructor.

Carefully fill the cell to the mark on the side tube with the radioactive silver nitrate solution, after making certain that the apparatus is fixed in a level, rigid position. Connect the leads to the circuit as illustrated in the diagram. Adjust the rheostat R so that a current about 0.01 ± 0.002 amps passes through the solution as measured by the ammeter A. The coulometer C may be either the silver or

[1] See Chapter IX.

copper type. After weighing the coulometer, reattach it and allow the current to pass for 120 minutes.

At the end of this time, cut off the current, and carefully close the connecting stopcock. Drain each compartment into a 100-milliliter beaker. Stir the solutions in the two beakers thoroughly with the glass tubes into which the electrodes

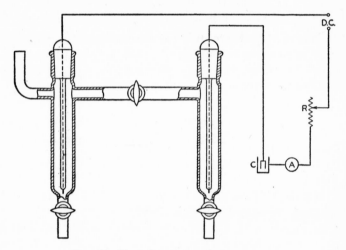

FIG. 12. Transference number apparatus.

are sealed. Measure in the liquid counting apparatus the activities of portions of the solutions in both compartments and a portion of the original solution. Reweigh the coulometer.

Calculations and Questions

1. What are the activities and normalities of the original, of the final cathode, and the final anode solutions? How much electricity was passed?

2. Knowing the volumes of the compartments, calculate the change in equivalents in each compartment.

3. Calculate the transference numbers of the cation and the anion. Compare these values with those as given in the literature.

4. How could the apparatus and the experimental procedure be improved to give more accurate results?

5. Design an experiment for transference number determination by the moving boundary method, using a radioindicator.

Other Suggested Experiments

Transference numbers of:

1. Chlorine in hydrochloric acid.
2. Iodine in potassium iodide.
3. Sodium in sodium nitrate.
4. Thallium in thallous sulfate.
5. Strontium in strontium chloride.
6. Silver in silver ammonium complex.

References

F. Daniels, J. H. Mathews, and J. W. Williams, "Experimental Physical Chemistry," McGraw-Hill Book Co., Inc., New York, 1941, pp. 232-240.

D. A. MacInnes, "Principles of Electrochemistry," Reinhold Publishing Corp., New York, 1939, pp. 59-95.

J. R. Partington in H. S. Taylor, "A Treatise on Physical Chemistry," D. Van Nostrand Co., Inc., New York, 1930, Vol. I, pp. 678-690.

A. P. Brady, *J. Am. Chem. Soc.* **70**, 911 (1948).

A. P. Brady and D. J. Salley, *J. Am. Chem. Soc.* **70**, 914 (1948).

XV. Distribution Ratios

OBJECT

Measurements are made on the distribution of a solute between two different phases, using a radioindicator. The distribution ratios are determined for iodine between water and carbon disulfide, chloroform, and carbon tetrachloride.

THEORY

If a volatile substance is shaken with a system of two immiscible liquids, A and B, it will dissolve and distribute itself between them according to a definite equilibrium. Provided that the solute obeys Henry's Law, its concentrations C_A and C_B, in each of the phases will be given by

$$C_A = k_1 p$$

$$C_B = k_2 p$$

where p is the vapor pressure in the gas phase in equilibrium with both A and B, and k_1 and k_2 are constants. Dividing the first equation by the second gives

$$\frac{C_A}{C_B} = \frac{k_1}{k_2} = K_d$$

The constant K_d is termed the distribution constant and gives the ratio of the solubilities in the two solvents. If the solute is associated or dissociated in either or both of the liquid phases, other equations must be utilized.

APPARATUS AND MATERIALS

Geiger-Mueller Counter, liquid counting apparatus, holder, saturated iodine solution containing two millicuries of radioactive iodine per liter,[1] three separatory funnels, seven fifty-milliliter volumetric flasks, carbon tetrachloride, carbon disulfide, chloroform, a one-milliliter pipette.

PROCEDURE

Into each of three separatory funnels place exactly one milliliter of the radioiodine solution and twenty-four milli-

[1] See Chapter IX.

liters of water. To the first add exactly twenty-five milliliters of carbon tetrachloride, to the second the same amount of carbon disulfide, and to the third a like quantity of chloroform. The funnels are stoppered and very carefully shaken. The layers are allowed to separate and then are run out into fifty-milliliter volumetric flasks. Each flask is then filled to the mark with the same solvent as it contains, and the solutions are thoroughly mixed. Into a fifty-milliliter flask, pipette one milliliter of the radioiodine solution, and dilute to the mark with water. Measure the activities of all seven of these solutions in the liquid counting apparatus.

Calculations and Questions

1. Calculate the distribution ratios for each of the systems. How do these compare with the literature values?

2. Derive formulas for the calculation of the distribution constant in each of the following cases:

(a) Phase I dissociation occurring—Phase II no molecular change occurring.

(b) Phase I no molecular change occurring—Phase II association occurring.

(c) Phase I dissociation occurring—Phase II association occurring.

3. Ten milliliters of an aqueous solution of iodine containing one milligram of iodine are shaken with two milliliters of carbon tetrachloride until equilibrium is established.

(a) From your constant calculate the iodine remaining in the aqueous layer. (b) Again the remaining aqueous layer (ten milliliters) is treated with two milliliters of carbon tetrachloride. Calculate the iodine remaining after this extraction. (c) Calculate the iodine remaining after five such extractions. (d) Calculate the iodine remaining in the aqueous layer after one extraction with ten milliliters of carbon tetrachloride. (e) Which process is more efficient, several successive extractions or one large extraction? (f) How does your conclusion apply to the washing of radioactive materials from glass apparatus?

Other Suggested Experiments

1. Distribution of hydrochloric acid between water and benzene, using radiochlorine.
2. Distribution of gallium and ferrous chlorides in ether.
3. Distribution of bromine between water and carbon tetrachloride, carbon disulfide, using radioactive bromine.
4. Distribution of silver nitrate between aniline and water.

References

F. Daniels, J. H. Mathews, and J. W. Williams, "Experimental Physical Chemistry," McGraw-Hill Book Co., Inc., New York, 1941, 143-146.

"International Critical Tables," McGraw-Hill Book Co., Inc., New York, 1928, Vol. III, pp. 418-435. *Ibid.* Vol. VI, pp. 309-312.

R. W. Knight and C. H. Hinselwood, *J. Chem. Soc.* 1927, 466.

D. C. Grahame and G. T. Seaborg, *J. Am. Chem. Soc.* 60, 2524 (1938).

A. A. Jakovin, *Z. phys. Chem.* B20, 19, (1896).

XVI. THE CHEMICAL EFFECTS OF RADIATION

OBJECT

This experiment has as its aim a demonstration of the principles of radiation chemistry.

THEORY

Radiation chemistry has been defined as the study of the interaction of the particles emitted in nuclear transitions with matter. The term "particles" includes alpha and beta particles, neutrons, fission recoils, protons, deutrons, gamma, and X-radiation. These particles in interacting with matter produce not only excitation but also ionization, thirty to thirty-five ev being required for each ionizing event. Generally, no more than a few molecules are chemically converted per ion-pair produced.

Yields in radiation reactions have been expressed in several different ways. The classical expression is the M/N ratio in which M is the number of molecules converted and N is the number of ion-pairs formed. There are several objections to this expression. The value of N is usually an approximation based upon the average energy required per process for an identical or similar substance in the gas phase. The ratio M/N does not have a constant scale of reference, since the average energy per process is different for different materials. Finally the use of this ratio implies that ionization is the origin of all radiation chemical reactions, which has not as yet been verified. More convenient and accurate expressions are G_1, the number of molecules converted per 100 ev, or G_2, the energy in electron volts needed for the conversion of one molecule.

The ionization of a molecule AB by high energy particles or radiation may be represented

$$AB \longrightarrow_{\text{vvvvvv}} AB^+ + e^-$$

The liberated electron then travels a distance of several hundred molecular diameters and comes to rest, either forming a negative ion

$$M + e^- \rightarrow M^-$$

or discharging a positive ion

$$M^+ + e^- \rightarrow M$$

where M may be AB or any other molecule. The succeeding reactions involving these secondary molecules depend upon their nature and the environmental conditions. Many types of reactions have been observed including dissociation, free radical formation, recombination, and new molecule formations.

Many substances have been subjected to radiation, chief among which are ionic crystals, organic materials, and aqueous solutions. In water we have an example of the effect of radiation upon covalently bonded inorganic compounds. The over-all reactions taking place may be summarized as:

$$2H_2O \rightarrow H_2O_2 + H_2$$
$$H_2O_2 \rightarrow H_2O + \tfrac{1}{2}O_2$$

The result of radiation on water depends largely upon the type of detection used and the specific radiation employed. The detailed equations may be written

$$H_2O \longrightarrow\hspace{-1em}\rightarrow H_2O^+ + e^-$$
$$H_2O^+ + aq \longrightarrow H_3O^+ + OH$$

and at a distance

$$H_2O + aq + e^- \rightarrow H + OH^-aq$$
$$and$$
$$H_3O^+ + e^- \rightarrow H + H_2O$$

The reactions

$$2H \rightarrow H_2$$
$$and$$
$$2OH \rightarrow H_2O_2$$

occur very frequently, the formation of hydrogen peroxide being most favorable in the regions where OH exists in a high concentration. In addition, the back reaction

$$H + OH \rightarrow H_2O$$

and the recombination reaction

$$H_2 + OH \rightarrow H_2O + H$$

take place in the solution. The extent to which these various reactions take place determines the value of G_1.

APPARATUS AND MATERIALS

100-milliliter glass-stoppered Erlenmeyer flask, a one-milliliter microburette, eighteen normal sulfuric acid, potassium iodide, 0.01 normal sodium thiosulfate, five millicuries of radioactive phosphorus,[1] starch solution.

PROCEDURE

To twenty milliliters of distilled water containing 0.2 grams of potassium iodide and five millicuries of radioactive phosphorus, add three milliliters of eighteen normal sulfuric acid, and dilute to twenty-five milliliters. Insert stopper, and allow this solution to stand in a dark place for one hour. Add a few drops of starch solution, and titrate the iodine with 0.01 normal sodium thiosulfate.

Place the solution in a dark place again, and after two-four- and sixteen-hour intervals repeat the titration. If it is desired to continue this experiment, successive titrations at appropriate intervals may be made.

Calculations and Questions

1. Calculate for each titration the number of ev required to produce one molecule of H_2O_2 using the average phosphorus-32 beta energy of 0.56 Mev.

2. What error is introduced by disregarding the beta energy lost due to beta radiation leaving the solution?

3. Explain the anomalous value obtained for the first titration.

4. Calculate the M/N ratio assuming thirty ev necessary to produce one ion pair.

[1] See Chapter IX.

References

M. Burton, *J. Phys. Colloid Chem.* **51**, 611, 786 (1947).

Symposium on Radiation Chemistry and Photochemistry, *J. Phys. Colloid Chem.* **52**, 437611 (1948).

S. C. Lind, "The Chemical Effects of Alpha Particles and Electrons," The Chemical Catalog Co., Inc., New York, 1928.

F. C. Lanning and S. C. Lind, *J. Phys. Chem.* **42**, 1229 (1938).

CHAPTER VII

PHYSICAL EXPERIMENTS

PHYSICAL EXPERIMENTS

XVII. Half-thicknesses of Gamma Rays

OBJECT

The purpose of this experiment is to indicate the difference between absorption of beta and gamma rays in matter. The half-values of gamma radiation from iodine-131 will be determined and the characteristic absorption curve will be drawn.

THEORY

Gamma radiation, unlike beta or alpha, is an electromagnetic wave. It is generally considered to be associated with the nuclei of excited atoms. One may consider an excited nucleus to be in several quantized energy states. When a transition from a higher to a lower energy level takes place, radiation in the form of photons or gamma radiation is observed. Gamma radiation is emitted by the nuclei of many stable atoms after absorption of a neutron. It often appears after the emission of an alpha or beta particle. Annihilation (the interaction between a positron and an electron) results in gamma radiation. Whenever an isomeric transition takes place, gamma radiation is emitted since there is no change in the charge of the nucleus. The phenomena of internal conversion result in this type of radiation. Bremsstrahlung and X-rays as softer components may also be observed in many transformations. In fact, nearly all the observable radiation from iron-55 seems to be X-rays.

Experimentally gamma radiation is usually detected from the secondary radiations produced by the interaction of gamma rays with matter. There are five different types of interactions, three of which are concerned with orbital electrons and two with the nucleus.

Pair production, the reverse of annihilation, occurs only when the incident ray has energy greater than twice the rest mass of the electron ($\sim$1.02 Mev). In this process the gamma ray, interacting with the nucleus, is entirely absorbed, and an electron pair (electron and a positron) appears. Interaction of this type depends upon the atomic number and increases both with energy and as Z^2.

The second type of interaction with the nucleus is photo-disintegration. This involves a transformation due to absorption of high energy radiation and depends upon the nuclear reaction that is initiated. The process occurs almost entirely with very high energy radiation and is not important in absorption or scattering.

Simple scattering, in which the electron remains in its orbit and the incident gamma ray is diverted without a change in wave length, has no effect on counting methods used to detect gamma radiation since no secondary radiation is formed. This process is similar to X-ray scattering in that diffraction patterns may be observed and are usually observed with low energy gamma rays.

A second process usually found with low energy gamma rays is photoelectric absorption. The incident radiation loses all its energy, and an orbital electron is ejected with an energy equal to the energy of the gamma ray minus the binding energy of the electron. High atomic numbers as well as low energy photons favor this process. This interaction has a probability that is proportional to Z^4/E^n, where n is an arbitrary number of one to three depending upon the wave length of the incident ray.

The collision of a gamma ray with an electron is termed the Compton recoil process. The transference of a portion of the gamma ray energy to the electron ejects it from its orbit. At the same time, the less energetic gamma recoils at an angle to its incident path. Both energy and momentum are conserved. Therefore, the recoil ray must have a longer wave length. In this process, as with beta ray scattering, the effect is proportional to the atomic number Z. For this reason Compton recoil is more dominant with medium energy gamma rays and in elements of low or medium atomic number.

Since the counting of gamma rays involves secondary electrons, it can be seen that the most important processes are Compton recoil, pair production, and photoelectric absorption. The loss in energy of an incident beam of gamma radiation can be shown to follow an exponential curve such as is expressed in Lambert's Law. Thus the loss per unit of thickness is a constant fraction. This constant fraction is known as the linear absorption coefficient, and the equation relating energy loss to thickness of absorber is

$$E = E_0 e^{-\mu x}$$

where x is the thickness and μ the linear absorption coefficient dependent upon the three processes mentioned above. E_0 and E are the energies of the radiation before and after passing through the absorber. The half-value thickness of gamma radiation can be denoted by an equation similar to the one used in beta absorption, thus: $x_{\frac{1}{2}} = 0.693/\mu$. Other coefficients that are often used are the mass absorption which is the linear coefficient divided by the density; electronic absorption, which is the absorption per electron and useful when Compton recoil is the greatest; and the atomic, which is the absorption per atom.

Unlike beta ray absorption, both the energy of the gamma radiation and the nature of the absorber influence the absorption. Because of this, only the mean absorption coefficient under specified conditions for the whole radiation needs to be determined. Once this has been done, reproducible results can be obtained by maintaining close control of the kind of absorber and the counting geometry. Another factor which enters into the counting of gamma radiation is the efficiency of the counter or ionization chamber.

Since only those rays that interact with charged particles producing secondary energetic electrons will be recorded, the thickness of the walls and the volume of the chamber will affect the efficiency of detection. Initially the number of electrons produced will increase with increasing wall thickness or interposed material. At the same time the thickness of matter that can be used is dependent upon the energy of the secondary electrons produced by the primary ray, since at a certain thickness these electrons will be absorbed within the interposed matter and not be recorded. Therefore, it can be deduced that the relatively thick wall ionization chambers will be the most efficient means of determining gamma radiation. Geiger-Mueller Counters can be used, but the efficiency is materially reduced. The number of events detected by the Geiger-Mueller tube is usually considered to be one per cent of the number entering the tube and is also dependent upon the geometry of the system as well as the construction of any shielding used to protect the tube from stray radiation.

APPARATUS AND MATERIALS

End-window Geiger-Mueller Counter, set of aluminum and lead absorbers, stop watch or clock, basic solution of sodium iodide approximately 0.01 molar containing two to three millicuries of radioactive iodine,[1] solution of silver nitrate (0.01 molar or less), sample holder with several shelves, 0.1-milliliter pipette and syringe, infrared lamp, squares of aluminum foil four centimeters on a side, cardboard mounting cards to fit sample holder, cellophane, Scotch tape, gamma sandwich.[2]

PROCEDURE

Prepare a mount of the radioiodine in a manner similar to that used in the Geiger-Mueller experiment. However, in order to insure that the iodine-131 remains on the plate, add a small drop of the silver nitrate solution to the plate before drying. After drying and covering the mount in the usual manner, determine the number of gamma counts per minute, using the gamma sandwich. Adjust the solution and prepare a mount which will give approximately 5,000 counts per minute.

Determination of Half-thickness. Beginning with the thinnest lead absorber, on the top shelf, determine the counts per minute obtained. Proceed through the set of absorbers, obtaining a value in counts per minute for each one. Do not try to count this plate without a lead absorber in place as the beta activity will be greater than the mechanical register can record.

Determination of Beta Range or Half-thickness with Gamma Rays Present. Prepare a mount analogous to

[1] See Chapter IX.
[2] See Chapter IX.

the one above but which will give approximately 10,000 counts per minute of beta (no absorber) on the second shelf. Determine the counts per minute for each aluminum absorber in the set.

Calculations and Questions

1. Plot the gamma counts per minute against the thickness of lead on semilog graph paper. Determine the half-value.

2. Plot the beta counts per minute against the thickness of the aluminum absorbers on semilog paper. Is it possible to determine the half-value of the gamma radiation from this curve? Does it agree with the value obtained for lead?

3. Subtract the gamma value from each point on the graph in question, and replot the residual counts per minute against absorber thickness. Determine the range and half-value for the iodine-131 beta.

4. How does the value for the range of the iodine-131 beta check with that calculated, using the formulas given in experiment III? Give reasons for any discrepancy.

5. Using the value of 0.37 Mev for the energy of iodine-131 gamma, determine the absorption coefficient μ for lead, copper, and aluminum.

6. Determine the counting efficiency of the Geiger tube for gamma rays, assuming that one beta and one gamma are emitted per disintegration of iodine-131.

7. Determine the millicuries of iodine-131 per unit volume of the standard solution. Consider the second shelf geometry as ten per cent.

Other Suggested Experiments

1. Determine the half-value thickness of iodine-131 gamma rays, using other metals as absorbers.

2. Determine the half-value thickness of iodine-131 gamma, using an ionization chamber or electroscope.

References

M. D. Kamen, "Radioactive Tracers in Biology," Academic Press Inc., New York, 1948.

E. Pollard and W. L. Davidson, "Applied Nuclear Physics," John Wiley and Sons, Inc., New York, 1942.

F. Rasetti, "Elements of Nuclear Physics," Prentice-Hall, Inc., New York, 1930.

J. M. Cork, "Radioactivity and Nuclear Physics," D. Van Nostrand Co., Inc., New York, 1947.

G. Hevesy and F. A. Paneth, "A Manual of Radioactivity," Oxford University Press, London, 1938.

XVIII. Long Half-life Measurements

OBJECT

Different radioactive materials decay with widely varying values for the half-life. The method employed for the measurement of the half-life of any particular isotope depends upon the length of the half-life. This experiment is designed to indicate a method for measuring long or very long half-lives.

THEORY

Calculations. The constancy of the disintegration rate has proven extremely valuable in the determination of the half-lives of radioactive materials with very long periods of decay. Because of this constancy, the number of atoms decaying in a specific period of time can be related to the total number of atoms present. In addition, if the rate of decay per mass unit is known, then the half-period and the average life expectancy may be calculated.

The number of atoms disintegrating per mass unit per second is equal to

$$\lambda N$$

if λ, the disintegration constant, is expressed in reciprocal seconds, and N in atoms per mass unit. The number of disintegrations per second may be obtained by a radio-activity measurement corrected for counter efficiency and back-scattering. The number of atoms in the amount of substance whose activity is measured can be calculated by weighing the sample and using the molecular weight of the substance and the Avogadro number. The disintegration constant may then be evaluated by the equation

$$\lambda = \frac{\lambda N}{N} \qquad (1)$$

which is simply the number of atoms disintegrating per second divided by the number of atoms present. The half-life, $t_\frac{1}{2}$, of the isotope is then calculated from the well-known formula

$$t_\frac{1}{2} = \frac{0.693}{\lambda} \qquad (2)$$

The equation for radioactive decay is exponential in character. Therefore, it implies that each atom has a definite probability of disintegrating at any particular moment and that the probability is proportional to the number of atoms existing at that time. Thus the life of any radioactive atom can have any value from zero to infinity. If this were not true, all the atoms would decay at the same time. Thus the gradual decay of radioactive atoms is explained. Another constant that has some value is called the average life-period. This constant may be shown to have a value of

$$\frac{1}{\lambda} \qquad (3)$$

Counter Efficiency Determinations. It is obvious that all particles emanating from a radioactive source will not enter the sensitive portion of a counting tube placed near it. In addition to the geometrical and absorption factors, back-scattering also has its effect. For these reasons, a substance similar to that being measured and of known weight and number of disintegrations is used to calibrate the counting tube. In this experiment the material used is uranium. A sample of this substance is measured, and the efficiency E of the counter is calculated by the formula:

$$E = \frac{D_{meas}}{D_{calc}}$$

where D_{meas} is the number of disintegrations per unit time measured by the counter, and D_{calc} is the same value calculated from the weight of the sample and the known number of disintegrations per unit time. From this efficiency other measurements may be corrected.

APPARATUS AND MATERIALS

Geiger-Mueller end-window counter and scaler, mounting cards, aluminum foil, one-milliliter pipette, standard solution of one molar of potassium chloride, solution containing about fifteen grams of uranyl uranate (weighed to the fourth place) per liter,[1] cellophane, Scotch tape, infrared lamp.

PROCEDURE

Pipette exactly one milliliter of the uranium solution onto each of three aluminum foils. Onto each of three more foils place exactly one milliliter of the potassium chloride solution. Dry all six samples under the heat lamp, mount on cards, cover with cellophane, and securely fasten each with Scotch tape. Each of the samples should be counted

[1] See Chapter IX.

for a length of time sufficient to give a total of 5,000 counts. Extreme care should be exercised to see that each sample is counted under conditions as constant as is possible.

Calculations and Questions

1. Average the three values for the uranium samples, compute the actual number of disintegrations taking place, and calculate the efficiency of the counting tube.

2. Look up the relative abundance of the potassium-40 isotope in naturally occurring potassium.

3. Average the results for the potassium samples, correct for efficiency, calculate the disintegration constant, the half-life, and the average life-period for potassium-40.

4. Discuss the errors involved in each of the following portions of the experiment: (a) efficiency determination; (b) half-life calculation.

5. Derive equations (1), (2), and (3).

6. Derive a formula for the weight in grams of one curie of a radioisotope. Calculate the grams per curie for potassium-40, uranium-238, radium-226, and cobalt-60.

Other Suggested Experiments

1. Determination of $t_{\frac{1}{2}}$ of lutecium-176.
2. Determination of $t_{\frac{1}{2}}$ of rhenium-187.
3. Determination of $t_{\frac{1}{2}}$ of rubidium-87.

References

S. Rowlands, *Nucleonics* 3, Nos. 3, 2-7 (1948).
H. D. Smythe and A. Hemmendinger, *Phys. Rev.* 51, 178 (1937).
A. D. Bramly and A. K. Brewer, *Phys. Rev.* 53, 502 (1938).
W. F. Libby and D. D. Lee, *Phys. Rev.* 55, 245 (1939).

XIX. Short Half-life Measurements

OBJECT

The determination of extremely long half-lives involves indirect calculations. However, the radioactive elements with half-lives in the range of hours to months may be determined directly from the change in counting rate. The object of this experiment is to determine the half-life of a radioelement by a graphical method.

THEORY

The theory of decay as presented in the experiment on long half-lives is the basis for the determination of long half-periods. However, when the half-period is short enough to fall easily within a span of a few days or months, the half-life may be determined by plotting the counting rate against time. Usually the intensity N is plotted as the ordinate, and the time t as the abscissa, on semilog graph paper. This graph then represents a plot of the equation:

$$\ln N = -\lambda t + C_1 \quad \text{or}$$

$$\log N = \frac{-\lambda t}{2.303} + C_2$$

where λ is the disintegration constant, C_1 and C_2 are integration constants, and t is the time. The slope of the straight line so produced is negative and equal to the disintegration constant divided by 2.303. From the disintegration constant, the half-life $t_{\frac{1}{2}}$ may be calculated from the relation

$$t_{\frac{1}{2}} = \frac{0.693}{\lambda}$$

APPARATUS AND MATERIALS

Geiger-Mueller Counter (end-window type), mounting cards, aluminum foil squares, cellophane, Scotch tape, 0.1-milliliter pipette, solution of sodium chloride containing two to three millicuries of radioactive sodium per liter,[1] infrared lamp, semilog graph paper.

PROCEDURE

Carefully transfer exactly 0.1 milliliter of the radioactive sodium chloride solution to each of three aluminum foil squares, and dry under the infrared lamp. Mount and secure each of the samples. Count each sample to obtain at least 5,000 counts. Note the time. Recount each sample every hour for the remainder of the laboratory period (it is advisable to prepare the sample as early as possible in the day in order to obtain several hourly counts). Recount the samples after twenty-four and forty-eight hours.

Plot the results on semilog graph paper.

Calculations and Questions

1. From the data obtained, what is the value of the half-life of radioactive sodium?

2. How does this value agree with the literature? What factors are involved to cause a variation from the accepted value?

References

S. Rowlands, *Nucleonics* 3, No. 3, 2 (1948).

E. Pollard and W. L. Davidson, Jr., "Applied Nuclear Physics," John Wiley & Sons, Inc., New York, 1942.

[1] See Chapter IX.

G. Hevesy and F. A. Paneth, "A Manual of Radioactivity," Oxford University Press, London, 1938.

XX. Very Short Half-life Measurements (Decay)

OBJECT

This experiment will demonstrate one method used in the determination of very short half-lives by the decay of active material.

THEORY

If a material decays with a short half-life, the activity can be determined by counting the total activity over a definite period of time and then at some short time later repeating this count. If this is done several times during the total decay of the material, it is possible to calculate the half-life.

Two paths are available for the determination of short half-lives. One outlined in this experiment depends upon a separation of the short-lived activity in pure form and a determination of its half-life from decay data. The other method involves the separation of the parent and the determination of the daughter or short-lived material by its growth. The latter method will be illustrated in Experiment XXI.

Many clever experiments have been devised for the determination of very short half-lives. Some of these require rather extensive equipment and are almost automatic in operation. Half-lives as short as microseconds have been determined. The accuracy involved in many of these experiments depends to a large extent upon the accuracy of the timing devices. Experiments that have been described in the literature involve determination of the activity of a volume of gas flowing past several counting or ionization devices at a known rate, determinations of the activity of a solid material mounted on a moving belt passing two or more sets of apparatus to indicate the activity after known intervals of time and determination by direct counting with a single Geiger Counter for definite times and at discrete time intervals.

If the activity of a sample has been determined for a definite period of time and after a lapse of some known time interval the activity has been redetermined for the original period, then the radioactive decay law can be applied to determine the half-life and the decay constant. However, the ratio of the counts after and before the time interval may be substituted for the ratio of atoms (N/No) and the time is the interval between the start of the two determinations. After the decay constant has been determined, the half-life may be found from the relation given in Experiment XVIII.

APPARATUS AND MATERIALS

Geiger-Mueller Counter and probe, rotating wheel (approximately ½ rpm), cardboard mounting card, cellophane, Scotch tape, infrared lamp, uranyl nitrate, thorium carrier solution (ten grams per liter), tantalum carrier solution (one gram per liter), 0.1 normal hydrofluoric acid, three-milliliter pipette, a one-milliliter pipette, 0.1-milliliter pipette and syringe.

PROCEDURE

Introduction. Whenever chemical processes are used for the separation of a short half-life material, the process must be as simple as possible and the time elapsed between the removal of the desired activity and the determination of the activity must be as short as possible.

Separation of Uranium-X_1. Using the method outlined in Experiment VI extract the uranium from ten grams of uranyl nitrate. (Recover the uranium.) Allow the activity in the aqueous phase to attain equilibrium (approximately ten minutes).

To the aqueous solution in a ten-milliliter volumetric flask, add three milliliters of the thorium carrier solution and one milliliter of the tantalum carrier solution. Add a slight excess of hydrofluoric acid, and dilute to the mark. Mix well, and allow the precipitate formed to settle. Without disturbing the precipitate remove 0.1 milliliter of the supernate, and prepare a mount as in Experiment II. Do not waste time between the precipitation and the counting of the sample.

Determination of Half-life of Uranium-X$_2$. Determine accurately the time required for one revolution of the wheel. Mark off on the wheel two points approximately one minute apart. Determine the time interval for this distance accurately. Mount the sample centered between these marks, and mount the probe directly over the top of the wheel with a known geometry.

Start the wheel rotating, and when the first mark passes under the probe start the counter. Allow counting to continue as the sample moves through the known time interval. Turn off the counter when the second mark passes, and allow the wheel to rotate through the remainder of the circle. When the sample arrives at the original starting point, the probe should be ready to start counting. Again count through the known time interval. If there is sufficient activity left, the count may be taken a third and even a fourth time. One hour after the first determination make a second determination, using the same supernatant liquid.

Calculations and Questions

1. Plot the data on semilog graph paper and determine the half-life.

2. Calculate the radioactive decay constant from the data, using several combinations of ratios obtained from the several counts. How does this compare with the literature value?

3. Determine the half-life from the decay constant as calculated in question 2. How does this compare with the literature value?

4. Devise another experiment by which very short half-life activities may be determined.

5. Explain the results of the second determination, particularly in regard to the activity found, if any.

References

S. Rowlands, *Nucleonics* 3, No. 3, 2 (1948).

H. G. J. Moseley, K. Fajans, *Phil. Mag.* 22, 629 (1911).

D. J. Hughes, J. Dobbs, A. Cohn, and D. Hall, *Phys. Rev.* 73, 111 (1943).

A. G. Ward, *Proc. Roy. Soc.* (A)181, 183 (1942).

A. C. English *et al., Phys. Rev.* 72, 253 (1947).

XXI. VERY SHORT HALF-LIFE MEASUREMENTS (GROWTH)

OBJECT

A second general method for the determination of very short half-lives will be evaluated in this experiment. The rate of regrowth of the daughter activity rhodium-106 from ruthenium-106 will be determined after the chemical separation of these elements.

THEORY

Genetic relationships between the several radioactive substances in a series of active decay products may be classified. The simplest condition and most important case are when the daughter activity has a half-life much shorter than the parent. If the separation of the daughter from the parent occurs, the daughter activity will regrow until an equilibrium exists. Equilibrium exists when the rate of decay of the daughter activity equals the rate of growth. At this time the following equilibrium holds:

$$\lambda_1 N_1 = \lambda_2 N_2 = \lambda_3 N_3 = \cdot \quad \cdot \quad \cdot \quad \cdot \quad \cdot \quad \cdot \quad \cdot \quad ,$$

where λ_1, λ_2, and λ_3 are the decay constants of a genetically related radioactive series, and N_1, N_2, and N_3 are the number of atoms of the several elements. Thus it is obvious that with any pair of parent-daughter activities the equilibrium quantities are inversely proportional to the fraction

$$\frac{\lambda_1}{\lambda_2} = \frac{N_2}{N_1}$$

If the radioactive element A_1 has a long half-life and A_2 has a much shorter half-life and if the two elements are separated at any time, the element A_2 will be regenerated until its mass is such that the above relations hold. During the period of regrowth, the element A_2 will decay with its own characteristic half-life. However, since only the fraction $\lambda_2 N_2$ will decay in any time interval t, there will be an increasing excess of N_2. The number of N_2 atoms not decaying in any time interval will increase until the rate of decay $\lambda_2 N_2$ equals the rate of formation of N_2 or $\lambda_1 N_1$. Then at this time the daughter activity will apparently decay at the same rate as the parent.

APPARATUS AND MATERIALS

Geiger-Mueller Counter and probe, concentrated phosphoric acid, potassium permanganate solution (five grams per liter), ruthenium carrier solution containing one millicurie of ruthenium-106 per liter,[1] six-molar sodium hydroxide solution, 0.1 molar stannous chloride, lead bricks, twenty-five-milliliter distillation flask, twenty-five-milliliter test tube.

PROCEDURE

Rhodium-106 Half-life. Set up distillation flask and receiver as shown in Figure 13. Pipette two milliliters of the permanganate solution, five milliliters of phosphoric acid,

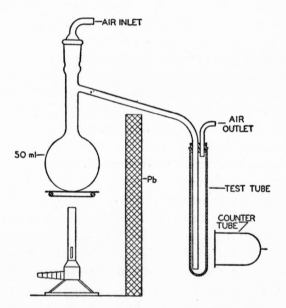

FIG. 13. Ruthenium distillation apparatus.

[1] See Chapter IX.

five milliliters of ruthenium solution, and three milliliters of water into the flask. Place twelve milliliters of six-molar sodium hydroxide solution into the test tube, and connect to the arm of the distillation flask. Insure that the end of the dip tube is nearly to the bottom of the test tube. Close the flask, and adjust the air to give one to two bubbles per second. Arrange lead shield and Geiger tube as shown in Figure 13. Determine the background count.

Start the Geiger-Mueller Counter, record the time, and the register reading. Heat the flask cautiously, then distill rapidly. During rapid distillation set the burner under the flask. While heating and distilling, record the register count every thirty seconds. Do not allow any bumping to occur. A yellow oil, ruthenium tetraoxide, should distill over. Heat until tube has been thoroughly rinsed. Remove the air bubbler from the flask, and discontinue the heating.

Continue to record the count every thirty seconds for ten minutes after the ruthenium has distilled or until the difference between readings has become approximately constant. Using the procedure outlined in Experiment II, determine the total activity of the sodium hydroxide solution and the original solution. (To the latter add a drop of stannous chloride and a drop of six-molar sodium hydroxide solution to the solutions on the aluminum foil before evaporating in order to maintain the ruthenium in a reduced state. Do not overheat the mount.)

Calculations and Questions

1. Plot the counts per minute against time on both linear and semilog graph paper.

2. Determine the half-life and decay constant of rhodium-106 from the graphs. How does your value compare with the literature? Explain any deviations.

3. How long a time was required for equilibrium to be attained?

4. If 0.005 microcurie of ruthenium-106 was present in the original flask, how many microcuries of rhodium-106 should be present in the distillate at the end of the experiment? (Assume quantitative distillation.)

5. How many atoms of rhodium-106 and ruthenium-106 are present in the equilibrium mixture?

6. With 0.005 millicurie of ruthenium-106 present in the distillate, determine the geometry of the counting apparatus.

7. Which isotope is being measured in this experiment? Explain your conclusion.

8. Determine the yield and explain how this determination could be made quantitative.

9. Outline another method for this determination.

References

J. D. Stranathan, "The Particles of Modern Physics," The Blakiston Co., Philadelphia, 1943, pp. 315-329.

H. G. J. Moseley and K. Fajans, *Phil. Mag.* 22, 629 (1911).

D. J. Hughes, J. Dobbs, A. Cohn, and D. Hall, *Phys. Ref.* 73, 111 (1943).

A. G. Ward, *Proc. Roy. Soc.* (A)181, 183 (1942).

A. C. English *et al, Phys. Rev.* 72, 253 (1947).

XXII. Friction Studies

OBJECT

An illustration of a radioactive indicator method for the measurement of wear is given. The wear of silver in frictional contact with several other metals is determined.

THEORY

Three major factors which contribute to frictional wear have been clearly recognized. These factors are interlocking of the irregularities of the sliding surfaces, adhesive forces between the atoms of the sliding materials, and contact electricity. The question as to which of these is the most important is yet to be settled.

It is generally assumed that the greater part of frictional work is transferred into thermal energy. Work is also consumed by cold working of the surfaces and by tearing of metal particles from the materials.

APPARATUS AND MATERIALS

Geiger-Mueller Counter, small silver block with radioactive silver plated onto one face,[1] two or three metal plates firmly secured to a heavy base, apparatus for sliding the silver block over the metal plates under a 100-gram load, oil.

PROCEDURE

Obtain a small silver block from the instructor. Place it in the friction apparatus with the radioactive face down. Adjust the apparatus so that it has approximately a 100-gram load. Bring the block into contact with one of the plates, and start the friction apparatus. Allow the two metals to slide for five minutes. Remove the plate, and measure its radioactivity. Repeat the sliding and measuring operations for ten five-minute periods.

Repeat the total procedure using a lubricant and a new radioactive silver block. If time allows, use plates of other metals.

Calculations and Questions

1. Construct graphs for each experiment, plotting radioactivity of the plate versus time.

---

[1] See Chapter IX.

2. Account for any strange results obtained in the graphs.

3. Obtain from the instructor the exact amount of silver plated onto the surface of the silver block, assume the counter fifteen per cent efficient, and calculate the actual number of atoms transferred after each frictional period for each of the experiments.

4. Suggest several industrial applications of radioactive frictional studies.

Other Suggested Experiments

1. Friction studies with zinc.
2. Friction studies with iron.
3. Friction studies with copper.

References

B. W. Sakmann, J. T. Burwell, and J. W. Irvine, Jr., *J. Applied Phys.* **15**, 459 (1944).

J. N. Gregory, *Nature* **157**, 443 (1946).

F. P. Bowden and L. Leben, *Proc. Roy. Soc. (London)* **A169**, 371 (1939).

XXIII. The Concentration of Radioisotopes by Recoil

OBJECT

The utility of the recoil process first used by Szilard and Chalmers for the preparation of radioactive substances of high specific activity is demonstrated. Bromobenzene solution is irradiated and the active isotopes of bromine are then separated.

THEORY

The capture of a slow neutron by most nuclei is accompanied by the emission of a gamma ray having an energy between three and six Mev. The resulting nucleus is generally beta or beta-gamma active. The momentum of the gamma ray is balanced by a recoil of the emitting nucleus, having a recoil energy E_R in electron volts, given by

$$E_R = \frac{533\,E^2}{M}$$

where E is the energy of the gamma ray in Mev, and M is the mass of the emitting nucleus in atomic weight units. In the majority of instances, this recoil energy is sufficient to disrupt one or more bonds of the molecule containing the active atom. It follows, then, that the modified atoms are usually found in a different chemical state than the unmodified ones and thus lend themselves to convenient chemical separations.

Bromine, as it is found in nature, consists of two isotopes, present in about equal proportions. These isotopes are of mass numbers 79 and 81, and they undergo the following reactions upon being bombarded with slow neutrons:

$$^{81}_{35}Br + ^{1}_{0}n \longrightarrow ^{82}_{35}Br + \gamma$$

$$^{79}_{35}Br + ^{1}_{0}n \longrightarrow ^{80}_{35}Br + \gamma$$

The newly formed isotopes then decay by the following schemes:

$$^{82}_{35}Br \xrightarrow{\;t^{1/2}\, -\, 34h\;} ^{82}_{36}Kr + \beta\ (0.465\ Mev) + \gamma\ (0.547\ Mev)$$

$$^{80}_{35}Br^{*} \xrightarrow{\;t^{1/2}\, -\, 4.4h\;} ^{80}_{35}Br + \gamma\ (49\ Kev)$$

$$\Big\downarrow t_{\frac12}\,18\ min$$

$$^{80}_{36}Kr + \beta^{-}\,(2\ Mev)$$

It will be noted the bromine-80 has two nuclear isomers, the one in the upper state being indicated by an asterisk.

Bromobenzene is used as the target substance in this experiment. When the bromine nucleus is activated by neutron capture, enough energy is supplied by the accompanying gamma ray recoil to eject the bromine. The ejected bromine is generally found in a water-soluble state (probably the bromide ion). The addition of a small amount of aniline has been shown to produce more water extractable activity.

APPARATUS AND MATERIALS

Geiger-Mueller Counter with tube, liquid counting apparatus, 100 milliliters of neutron-bombarded bromobenzene,[1] 250-milliliter separatory funnel, 0.10 molar potassium bromide, small radium-beryllium neutron source.

PROCEDURE

Obtain 100 milliliters of the irradiated bromobenzene from the instructor. Transfer enough of this solution to the liquid counting apparatus to fill it, and measure the activity. Discard this solution, and wash out the tube thoroughly. Transfer the remainder of the bromobenzene-aniline solution to a small separatory funnel, and add to it thirty milliliters of 0.10 molar potassium bromide. Shake well and allow the two phases to separate. Draw off the nonaqeous layer, transfer a portion of it to the liquid counting apparatus, and determine the activity. Following this, make successive activity measurements on a portion of the water phase every ten minutes for one and one-half hours. All of these measurements should be carried out in a minimum of time to avoid error introduced by radioactive decay.

Calculations and Questions

1. Calculate the approximate percentage of activity extracted by the potassium bromide solution.

2. Discuss the error introduced by the time difference between the measurements. How can this be corrected?

[1] See Chapter IX.

3. What is the apparent half-life of the potassium bromide extracted activity? Why does it differ from eighteen minutes?

4. Assuming that the gamma ray energy is 5.1 Mev, calculate the recoil energy of a bromine-80 atom.

5. Calculate the activity which would have been produced by irradiation of the bromobenzene for an infinite length of time.

6. What is the nuclear reaction by which the neutrons were produced?

Other Suggested Experiments

1. Irradiation of phosphates.
2. Irradiation of arsenates.
3. Irradiation of other halogen compounds.
4. Irradiation of other organic halides.

References

E. Fermi, E. Amaldi, *et al, Proc. Roy. Soc. (London)* **A149,** 522 (1935).

W. F. Libby, *J. Am. Chem. Soc.* **62,** 1930 (1940).

L. Szilard and T. A. Chalmers, *Nature* **134,** 462 (1934).

U. Drehmann, *Z physik chem.* **B53,** 227 (1943).

O. Erbacher and K. Phillipp, *Z. physik Chem.* **A176,** 169, (1936).

R. B. Duffield and M. Calvin, *J. Am. Chem. Soc.* **68,** 1129 (1946).

XXIV. Separation of Nuclear Isomers by Recoil

OBJECT

This experiment is designed to illustrate the method by which nuclear isomers may be separated. Separation of the two states of the bromine-80 nucleus is effected.

THEORY

A compound suitable for the application of the Szilard-Chalmers method of concentration is prepared from a mixture of the two isomers to be separated. The decay of the isomer in the upper state to that in the lower state may provide sufficient energy to eject the decayed atom from its compound. The daughter activity may then be separated by a chemical process, since it probably exists in a different state of combination.

Even if the energy of the transition is not sufficient to disrupt the bond, the method may not fail because of two other possibilities. First, the gamma rays from the upper state are highly internally converted, giving considerable added recoil, usually comparable to chemical bond energies. Second, should the recoil still fail to break the bond, the energy given to the bond may activate it enough so that it will undergo chemical reaction with another molecule introduced specifically for this purpose. In the latter case, the lower isomeric state will be found in the product of the chemical reaction.

In this experiment, normal butyl bromide is prepared containing a very small amount of bromine-82 and the two nuclear isomers of bromine-80. When the upper state bromine-80 atom emits a gamma ray and drops in energy to the lower state, the bromine-80 atom is ejected and exists in a water-soluble chemical state. Therefore, the two isomeric states may be effectively separated.

APPARATUS AND MATERIALS

Geiger-Mueller Counter, liquid counting tube, fifty milliliters of radioactive potassium bromide solution,[1] acetone, butyl bromide, benzene, 250-milliliter separatory funnel.

PROCEDURE

Obtain fifty milliliters of the radioactive mixture from the instructor, place it in a 250-milliliter separatory funnel,

[1] See Chapter IX.

and add thirty-five milliliters of benzene. Shake well, allow the layers to separate, and draw off each layer into a beaker. Fill the liquid counting tube with the benzene solution, and measure the activity every ten minutes for one and one-half hours, taking as zero the time when the extraction was made.

Return the benzene from the counting tube to the beaker. Add to it twenty-five milliliters of acetone and five milliliters of water. Shake well in a separatory funnel, and draw off the water layer. Measure its activity every ten minutes for one hour.

Calculations and Questions

1. Plot the activity of the sample against the time in minutes on semilog graph paper for both measurements.

2. Calculate the half-life of the lower state of the bromine-80 nucleus.

3. Calculate the efficiency of isomer separation.

4. Explain any peculiarities in the graphs and the half-life value.

5. Write full physical and/or chemical equations for each process in the experiment.

Other Suggested Experiments

1. Separation of the tellurium nuclear isomers.
2. Separation of the selenium-83 isomers.

References

E. Segre, R. S. Halford, and G. T. Seaborg, *Phys. Rev.* **55**, 321 (1938).

L. J. LeRoux, C. S. Lu, and S. Sugden, *Nature* **143**, 517 (1939).

D. C. DeVault and W. F. Libby, *Phys. Rev.* **55**, 322 (1938).

G. T. Seaborg and J. W. Kennedy, *Phys. Rev.* **55**, 410 (1938).

J. R. Arnold, N. Sugarman, *J. Chem. Phys.* **15**, 703 (1947).

CHAPTER VIII

BIOLOGICAL EXPERIMENTS

Chapter VIII

BIOLOGICAL EXPERIMENTS

XXV. Plant Radioautographs

OBJECT

The action of radiations on a photographic emulsion to indicate tracer distribution is demonstrated. Phosphorus deposition in the leaves and stem of a young tomato plant is studied.

THEORY

When a radioactive substance is administered to an organism, the material distributes itself among the various parts of the organism in a fashion typical of the experimental conditions. After a lapse of time to allow distribution to be attained, the organism is washed free of any contamination and allowed to dry. A section of the suspected radioisotope bearing region is prepared and placed in contact with a photographic film. The radioactive particles emitted by the isotopes deposited in certain places in the section will expose the film. After development, all regions containing radioactive substance will be darkened giving a picture of the tracer distribution. This picture is termed a "radioautograph."

Generally X-ray films are used, but there are now on the market several specially prepared nuclear particle photographic emulsions. The exposure time required is dependent upon the film, the amount of radioactive substance, the nature and energy of the radiations, and the method used

193

for preparing the substance and placing it in contact with the film. Beta particles seem to be better suited for radio-autographs than do gamma rays. Various estimates have been made of the number of particles necessary to produce a satisfactory image. These vary from 10^6 to 10^9 beta particles per square centimeter of film. The film is developed with the developer and procedure recommended by the manufacturer of the film.

The radioautographic technique is excellent for demonstrating the localization of activity, but there are three factors which limit it considerably. First, the radiation from a point source of tracer atoms is emitted in all directions, and hence a sharp image cannot be obtained. Second, the amount of radiosubstance administered must be small enough so that the tissue is not damaged. Third, the method is limited by the grain of the photographic emulsion which determines resolution and sensitivity.

The radioautograph shows semiquantitatively where an element deposits, but its chemical form and the method of deposition cannot be read. Other methods must be utilized to obtain this information.

APPARATUS AND MATERIALS

A liquid counting apparatus and Geiger-Mueller Counter, a reliable brand of X-ray film, black paper, glass plates, developer, fixer, week-old tomato plants in small clay pots, 0.01-molar solution of disodium hydrogen phosphate containing two to three millicuries of phosphorus-32 per liter,[1] large beaker, two thirty-milliliter crucibles, five normal hydrochloric acid, two fifty-milliliter volumetric flasks.

[1] See Chapter IX.

PROCEDURE

Secure a small tomato plant growing in soil contained in a clay pot, and place it in a large beaker. With a glass rod make a hole about thirty millimeters deep and fifteen millimeters in diameter in the soil alongside the stem of the plant. Pour into this hole about five milliliters of the radioactive phosphorus solution, followed by five milliliters of water. Allow the plant to stand twenty-four hours.

Carefully cut off a top portion of the plant containing three or four leaves. Wash this thoroughly in water for a minute. Allow the excess water to drain, and then place it against the black paper which is wrapped around a piece of X-ray film. Press the plant tightly against the paper with a glass plate, and then anchor it firmly with some heavy object. After an hour's exposure, remove the film and develop it according to the manufacturer's instructions.

Cut off the plant at the surface of the dirt, and with forceps and a knife separate the stem material from the leafy portion. Place each of these in thirty-milliliter crucibles, cover, and ash in a furnace at 550° C for one-half hour. Allow the residues to cool, dissolve them in five normal hydrochloric acid, and transfer the resulting solutions to fifty-milliliter volumetric flasks. Dilute the liquids in the flasks to fifty-milliliter volume with water. Measure the activities of each of these solutions in the liquid counting apparatus.

Calculations and Questions

1. Where does the phosphorus appear to accumulate in the plant?
2. Calculate the ratio of phosphorus in the stem material to that in the leafy substance for the leaf that was measured.
3. Explain why betas are better for radioautographs than are gammas.

Other Suggested Experiments

1. Deposition of phosphorus in other plants.
2. Deposition of zinc in plants.
3. Deposition of strontium in plants.
4. Transport and uptake of sodium in plants.

References

D. I. Arnon, P. R. Stout, and R. Sipes, *Am. J. Botany* **27**, 791 (1940).

M. D. Kamen, "Radioactive Tracers in Biology," Academic Press, Inc., New York, 1947, pp. 251-257.

A. Gorbinan, *Nucleonics* **2**, No. 6, 30-43 (1948).

J. Sacks, *Chem. Rev.* **42**, 411 (1948).

XXVI. EXCRETION AND DEPOSITION STUDIES

OBJECT

Since phosphorus is one of the important elements in the body metabolism, this experiment has been designed to indicate what happens to a portion of the phosphorus that is taken into the body. Radioautographs of a bone and tooth will be prepared. The amount of phosphorus-32 deposited in the average skeleton and the quantity of phosphorus-32 eliminated in the first twenty-four hours will be determined.

THEORY

Because radioactive phosphorus has been the most readily available artificial radioisotope in quantity, there has been a considerable amount of research using this activity to determine the metabolism of phosphorus in the body. There are two methods whereby active phosphorus may be introduced into the body. One procedure is to give the activity orally and the other by injection either intravenously or subcutaneously. The latter techniques seem to give more effective retention of the artificial isotope than the former since a considerable variation of the retention of phosphorus-32 in rats has been reported for oral administration.

Assimilation of phosphorus by the body depends upon many factors too numerous to mention in this experiment. However, since most of the element in the feces results from unassimilated food and endogenous metabolism, the ratio of phosphorus resulting from endogenous metabolism can be determined from the ratio of the specific activities of the phosphorus-32 in the feces to that in the urine.

The function of phosphorus in the body has been rather thoroughly investigated. It is involved in several exchanges and synthesis reactions. There appears to be a very rapid turnover of phosphorus in the liver, digestive tract, and muscle. However, the bone which contains a large amount of phosphorus seems to have a low turnover. Even though the specific activity of the phosphorus in the bone may be low, the total activity retained has been found to be high, in fact the highest of any body organ. The retention of phosphorus in the bone is undoubtedly due to the apatite structure. Therefore, since the release of phosphorus from the bone is low, the retention of phosphorus-32 will be high, and it has been found that when phosphorus-32 is used in long-term experiments most of the retained activity will be found in the bone.

Phosphate absorbed into the blood stream rapidly diffuses into the extracellular space. Thus, short-time experiments will not be affected too much due to losses in excretions.

Researches involving the use of phosphorus in the body

have revealed that this element is involved in one of the most important mechanisms for storage and energy for synthesis. This reaction is termed *phosphorylation*. Inorganic phosphate does not exchange with organic phosphate when labeled inorganic phosphate is agitated in the same phase with such compounds as nucleic acid, casein, or glycerophosphate. However, labeled phosphate appears in the body in ester form, and this is the evidence for the synthesis reactions in the body.

Active phosphate begins to exchange with bone phosphate very rapidly, probably due to the close contact with the various lymphatic liquids. Phosphorus is deposited in the spongy structure of the teeth since this is in better contact with the lymph than is the enamel.

Cells that are rapidly metabolizing appear to pick up phosphate more rapidly than other tissues. The liver exchanges phosphates with the intracellular liquid more rapidly than tissues like the brain. Entry of phosphate into the cell relies, to a great extent, upon the carbohydrate metabolic activity. Phosphorus is also involved in protein metabolism through nucleic acids and nucleo-proteins.

APPARATUS AND MATERIALS

Two rat femurs, feces of rat, blotting paper from the bottom of the cage, coping saw, X-ray film, black paper, developer, fixer, five normal hydrochloric acid, three fifty-milliliter volumetric flasks, three fifty-milliliter crucibles, muffle furnace, Geiger-Mueller Counter and probe, liquid counting apparatus or end-window counter, jawbone and tooth of rat.[1]

[1] See Chapter IX.

PROCEDURE [1]

Introduction. Obtain from the instructor both femurs and the jawbone of a rat that has been fed 100 microcuries of phosphorus-32. Also obtain the feces and the blotting paper from the bottom of the cage. Handle these materials carefully as they all contain radioactive phosphorus.

Radioautographs of the Bone and Tooth. Split the jaw-bone containing an incisor and one of the femurs with a coping saw. Be careful of the dust as it is radioactive. This operation should be done in a hood with water or alcohol dripping on the saw to keep the dust wet. Leave the incisor in the jawbone but take only a portion of it such that the final preparation will have one flat surface for the best con-tact with the film. The pulp-cavity of the tooth should be evident.

Determine the activity from one surface of the bones, and calculate the time required to obtain 10^7 disintegrations per square centimeter of film. Prepare the radioautograph, and develop it according to the instruction in Experiment XXV.

Total Activity in Bony Structure. Ash one of the femurs in a fifty-milliliter crucible and proceed as in Experiment XXV. Measure the activity if possible, using the liquid counting apparatus. If the activity is too low to give an accurate count, prepare a mount, and evaluate the total activity, using the end-window Geiger tube.

Phosphorus in the Feces. Ash the feces, and determine the phosphorus-32 activity in the same manner as above.

Total Activity in the Urine. Carefully ash the blotting paper, and determine the phosphorus-32 content in the same manner as above.

[1] See Chapter IX.

Calculations and Questions

1. From the radioautograph of the jawbone and tooth determine where the phosphorus is predominant.

2. Determine what portion of the femur appears to contain the most phosphorus.

3. Assuming that the femur is two per cent of the total bony structure, determine the amount of phosphorus-32 absorbed in the bone. What percentage is this of the 100 microcuries originally given to the rat? The instructor will supply the zero time.

4. Calculate the per cent phosphorus-32 lost in the urine.

5. Calculate the per cent loss in the feces.

6. Explain why the total phosphorus-32 recovered does not equal the amount administered.

7. Outline an experiment for the determination of the specific activity of the phosphorus-32 in both the feces and urine.

Other Suggested Experiments

1. Deposition of strontium in the bone.

2. Deposition of calcium in the bone.

References

M. D. Kamen, "Radioactive Tracers in Biology," Academic Press, Inc., New York, 1947.

M. L. Manly and S. R. Levy, *J. Biol. Chem.* **139**, 35 (1941).

W. E. Cohn and D. M. Greenberg, *J. Biol. Chem.* **130**, 625 (1939).

D. H. Copp and D. M. Greenberg, *J. Nutrition* **29**, 261 (1945).

M. O. Schultze and S. J. Simmons, *J. Biol. Chem.* **142**, 97 (1942).

O. DuPont, I. Ariel, and S. L. Warren, *Am. J. Syphilis, Gonorrhea, Venereal Diseases* **26**, 96 (1942).

XXVII. Deposition of Iodine in the Thyroid

OBJECT

The objective of this experiment is to indicate the absorption of iodine in the thyroid and its specificity.

THEORY

Iodine and its relation to the thyroid have been the subject of great interest to both biochemists and medical researchers. With the advent of radioiodine the rate at which iodine was absorbed by the thyroid was shown to be extremely rapid. It has been determined that there is a substantial concentration in the thyroid within a few minutes after intravenous injection. Other experiments have indicated that the maximum concentration occurs between fourteen and fifty hours after the dose was administered.

The greatest interest in the use of radioiodine has been the relation of the capacity of the thyroid to concentrate iodine and convert the inorganic to organic iodide in respect to the effect of alterations of the state of the thyroid function. Also considerable interest has been shown in tracing antithyroid substances, such as thiouracil, with particular emphasis on the action of these substances.

Di-iodotyrosine has been shown to be the principal form in which iodine is stored. However, iodine has been found in the thyroid as inorganic iodide and as thyroxine. The conversion from the initially inorganic fixed iodine to the organic forms appears to be quite rapid. Several workers have reported that inorganic active iodine has been found in the thyroid even when the active material was administered only in the organic form, thus indicating that the organic is converted to inorganic before being fixed by the thyroid.

The collecting capacity of the thyroid has been determined in relation to the functional activity of the gland and has been found to diminish when the activity diminishes and increase when the activity increases. The collecting capacity has also been investigated in relation to goitrogenic substances. These materials can be classified according to manner in which the capacity of the gland to collect and its ability to convert the iodine.

APPARATUS AND MATERIALS

One healthy rat or rabbit, syringe and needle for injection, several lead bricks, 0.1-milliliter solution containing ten microcuries of iodine-131 in a buffered isotonic saline solution at a pH of 7.0,[1] Geiger-Mueller tube.

PROCEDURE [2]

(Two students should work together on this experiment)

Firmly secure the animal to the bench surface and place lead bricks around it so that any radiation from the point of injection cannot reach the Geiger-Mueller tube which is placed near the thyroid of the animal. Inject 0.1 milliliter of the prepared iodine solution, containing ten microcuries of iodine, intravenously in one of the hind legs of the animal. Note the time at which this was done, and start the counter. Record the counter reading every thirty seconds for the first ten minutes and then every two minutes for thirty minutes. Continue to take readings for the remainder of the class period at intervals of ten minutes.

Near the end of the class period shield the thyroid of the animal and survey the rest of its body with the Geiger tube. Record any activity and its location.

Calculations and Questions

1. Plot the rate of absorption of iodine-131.

2. Determine the time required for the iodine to appear first in the thyroid.

[1] See Chapter IX.
[2] See Chapter IX.

3. Would you expect the iodine to concentrate in any other part of the body in a healthy and in a diseased animal? Explain your conclusions.

References

I. Perlman, M. E. Morton, and I. L. Chaikoff, *J. Biol. Chem.* **139**, 449 (1941).

M. E. Morton, I. Perlman, and I. L. Chaikoff, *J. Biol. Chem.* **140**, 603 (1941).

A. Taurog and I. L. Chaikoff, *J. Biol. Chem.* **163**, 323 (1946).

A. Taurog and I. L. Chaikoff, *J. Biol. Chem.* **169**, 49 (1947).

M. C. Barry, *J. Biol. Chem.* **175**, 179 (1948).

D. S. Riggs and E. B. Man, *J. Biol. Chem.* **134**, 193 (1940).

Jacob Sacks, *Chem. Rev.* **42**, No. 2, 411 (1948).

XXVIII. Body Fluid Volume and Absorption

OBJECT

The ease with which body fluid volume measurements can be made is demonstrated, using radioactive sodium. Also, an absorption curve is determined.

THEORY

Sodium chloride, injected intravenously, equilibrates rapidly with extracellular body fluids. If the injected salt contains radiosodium, its course may be followed, and the volume of the body fluid may be calculated. When equilibrium has been reached (the time varies with the animal), the following equation may be used to calculate the extracellular fluid volume V:

$$U + V = \frac{C_0}{C_E}$$

in which C_0 is the activity of a given volume, U, of the originally injected solution, and C_E is the activity of the same volume of solution taken from the animal's body after equilibrium has been reached. Care must be taken not to draw the equilibrium sample too long after the injection, since absorption of the material into the cells takes place rapidly. By several successive removals of fluid, absorption may be followed.

APPARATUS AND MATERIALS

Geiger-Mueller Counter, liquid counting apparatus, a full-grown rat, a 0.01-molar sodium chloride solution containing one millicurie of radioactive sodium per liter,[1] syringe and hypodermic needle, two fifty-milliliter volumetric flasks.

PROCEDURE

Transfer exactly one milliliter of the radioactive solution to a fifty-milliliter volumetric flask, dilute to the mark with water, and mix well. Place a portion of this solution in the liquid counting apparatus, and measure its activity. Draw into the syringe exactly one milliliter of the radioactive sodium chloride solution, and inject it intravenously into the rat, starting a stop watch at the same time. After an elapse of five minutes withdraw from the animal a one-milliliter sample of blood, using the syringe and needle. Dilute this one milliliter to exactly fifty milliliters in a volumetric flask, and mix thoroughly. Measure the activity of a portion of this solution. Repeat the withdrawal and measurement every thirty minutes for the following two hours.

[1] See Chapter IX.

Calculations and Questions

1. Construct a graph plotting activity against time for the extracted portions of blood, correcting for the decay of the radioactive sodium.
2. Calculate the extracellular fluid volume.
3. Discuss the errors inherent in this experiment.

Other Suggested Experiments

1. Utilization of sulfates labeled with radioactive sulfur.
2. Absorption and excretion of zinc with radioactive zinc.
3. Use of arsenates with radioactive arsenic.

References

M. D. Kamen, "Radioactive Tracers in Biology," Academic Press, Inc., New York, 1947, pp. 213-220.

L. Halen, G. Hevesy, and O. Rebbe, *Biochem. J.* 33, 7549 (1939).

J. F. Manery and A. B. Hastings, *J. Biol. Chem.* 127, 657 (1939).

W. E. Cohn and E. T. Cohn, *Proc. Soc. Exptl. Biol. Med.* 41, 445 (1939).

E. H. Quimby, *Nucleonics* 1, No. 4, 2 (1947).

CHAPTER IX

SPECIAL PREPARATIONS

CHAPTER IX

SPECIAL PREPARATIONS

INTRODUCTION

Radioactive isotopes may be obtained either in a solid or solution form. The solids as obtained from Oak Ridge National Laboratory are termed *irradiation units* and consist of a weighed amount of a particular compound. These compounds may contain one or more radioactive isotopes, depending upon the compound bombarded and upon the normal impurities present in chemically pure substances. If this type of material is used, the instructor will have to dissolve the compound supplied in a suitable solvent with due regard to the possible volatility of certain elements. The compounds used in this text will not require special attention because of the volatility of any of the elements, since those that are likely to cause difficulty should be obtained in solution form.

After the material has been dissolved, the solution should be made up to a known volume and assayed for the active elements. From these data and the information given on the packing slip, the instructor can prepare the tracer solutions by adding the proper volume of the active solution to a known volume of the standard inactive salt solution.

If the material is obtained as a solution, it will contain a known amount of active material in the presence of no added carrier or a small known amount depending upon the particular isotope obtained. This information is listed on the packing list, which should be consulted before any tracer preparations are made. In this case the instructor may pipette the correct volume to contain the required activity directly from the shipment and transfer it to the standard solution. Then the standard solution should be assayed for the radioelement. If the volume of the liquid received is small as it sometimes will be, the instructor may wish to dilute this material and assay it before making up the active tracer preparation for the laboratory.

In the following pages the tracer solutions or materials needed are listed according to the active isotope, followed by the solutions that are required, the compound and form of the activity purchased, the method of preparing the tracer solution, and any special methods that may be required.

The instructor may not have the facilities for preparation of some of the following solutions; however other materials may be available and similar procedures should be used in order to prepare the active solutions. It is possible in most instances to substitute other active substances for those described in the experiments as is noted under the heading "Other Suggested Experiments."

In many instances, the activities as specified in the experiments will have to be altered to suit the detection apparatus used.

Bromine-80-82

Bromobenzene containing radioactive bromine; 0.001-molar potassium bromide solution   (Prepared by the instructor as below)

Extreme care must be exercised in handling the highly active Ra-Be neutron source. The neutrons and gamma rays emitted are very energetic and therefore are excessively injurious to tissue. The source should always be manipulated with long-handled tongs, and the best protection against the radiations is distance. Therefore, one should remain in the presence of the unshielded source only as long as it is absolutely necessary.

In a segregated area or room remove the neutron source from its shield, and immediately lower it into the center of 1,000-milliliter bottle containing 900 milliliters of bromobenzene and fifty milliliters of aniline. A long string should be attached to the source in order to facilitate suspension and removal. Leave the room immediately and post a warning sign on the door. Allow the source to remain in the solution for an hour. Return to the room, remove the source, wash it, and replace in the shield. Use this bromobenzene solution for Experiment XXIII. For the preparation needed in Experiment XXIV, proceed as follows.

Extract the ejected active bromine with twenty milliliters of the 0.001-molar potassium bromide solution. Add to this extracted material 180 milliliters of acetone and 200 milliliters of normal butyl bromide. Allow this mixture to stand for one hour with frequent shaking.

Carbon-14

> 0.05-molar potassium oxalate solution
> Carbon-14 is obtained as barium carbonate

Barium carbonate containing radioactive carbon-14 may be obtained from the Atomic Energy Commission. To one millicurie of this substance is added one gram of inert barium carbonate. To this mixture is added, dropwise, dilute hydrochloric acid. The liberated radioactive carbon dioxide is passed over a suitable drying agent and then into an evacuated flask containing two grams of molten potassium and two grams of coarse sand. The carbon dioxide is allowed to react with the mixture for about one-half hour. The flask is then cooled, and the excess potassium is carefully decomposed by addition of water. The resulting solution is acidified to decompose the carbonate formed as a by-product, filtered, and neutralized. To it is then added 500 milliliters of approximately 0.050-molar potassium oxalate solution.

Quantities of potassium trioxalatoferrate(III) and potassium trioxalatochromate(III) are prepared as described in Inorganic Synthesis, Vol. I. From these approximately 0.050-molar solutions are prepared.

Iodine-131

> 0.01 molar sodium iodide (basic)
> isotonic solution of sodium chloride containing active iodine
> saturated iodine solution

Iodine-131 is obtained as a basic solution of sodium iodide, usually at a pH eight to nine. Since this material has no added carrier, care must be exercised to keep it in the basic condition until after carrier has been added, otherwise the iodine will be lost quite rapidly. The 0.01-molar sodium iodide solution can be prepared by adding the required volume of the material purchased to a basic solution of 0.01 molar sodium iodide. If a pH greater than seven is maintained, no difficulties should be encountered.

The isotonic solution is prepared by adding the active iodine solution to a 0.85 per cent sodium chloride solution and adjusting the pH to 7.2. Before injection this solution should be sterilized by the usual methods.

The saturated iodine solution should be prepared by adding the active iodine-131 solution (using the smallest possible volume) to the saturated iodine solution.

If it is desired to investigate the iodine metabolism further, the experiment may be extended by collecting the urine excreted during a specified time and analyzing this material by one of the techniques described in Chapter V. To complete the iodine metabolism studies, the thyroid may be removed and the iodine determined, using the method described by A. Taurog and I. L. Chaikoff [1] modified to fit the particular counting equipment available. If the thyroid is to be used in an experiment it should be prepared by the instructor.

Iron-59

0.1 molar ferric chloride

The iron-59 may be obtained as a solution of ferric chloride in hydrochloric acid or as metallic iron. In either case the material will contain both iron-55 and iron-59. The iron-55 will not cause any difficulty in the experiment since the radiations are very soft. However, the radiations are X-rays, and therefore protection should be provided. If the iron is obtained as the metal, it may be dissolved in hydrochloric acid and the necessary volume of this solution added to the standard iron solution to give the tracer material.

If the material is received in solution form, the packing list should be checked for the concentration of inert iron and the specific activity noted before the material is added to the standard solution.

Phosphorus-32

0.01 molar disodium hydrogen phosphate phosphoric acid

[1] *J. Biol. Chem.* **163**, 323 (1946).

Radioactive phosphorus is shipped in several forms. The best material to obtain would be the solution as phosphoric acid (~pH 4) in which a small amount of carrier has been added in order to maintain the phosphorus in solution. It is commonly known that in solutions of phosphates, particularly in tracer quantities as used in radioactive work, the phosphate will precipitate on glass vessels rather easily. Therefore one must be extremely cautious when using pure tracer or materials to which no carrier has been added, because the ever-present calcium will precipitate the phosphorus. Also impurities such as iron or other trivalent elements with insoluble phosphates that are found as contaminants in water or chemicals will also remove the phosphorus, particularly in the neighborhood of pH 7.

The solution as received may be added to the standard disodium hydrogen phosphate to prepare the tracer solutions. Two experiments require the use of the material as acquired. If the instructor schedules the experiments properly, the more dilute solutions (less activity) may be obtained by allowing the more concentrated ones to decay to the proper value, thus obtaining material for several experiments from the same original radioisotope shipment.

Obtain a rat which has had a lack of water, and place it on the wire bottom of the cage. In the pan under the cage, place blotting paper which will absorb the urine and collect the feces. Two milliliters of water containing 100 microcuries of phosphorus-32 should be fed the rat, using a stomach tube. After twenty-four to forty-eight hours, the animal is sacrificed, and the femurs and mandible are dissected out. The feces is brushed carefully off the blotting paper into a beaker. Save the blotting paper.

Radium-D, -E, -F

Solution of radium-D, -E, -F 0.5 normal in hydrochloric acid

There are two convenient sources of mixtures of radium-D, -E, and -F. One of these is enriched radiolead compounds which may be purchased from several Canadian companies. It is only necessary to dissolve a small amount of the enriched lead nitrate in about 250 milliliters of water. The proper amount of hydrochloric acid is added, and the precipitate that is formed will not interfere with the presence of the required radioactive substances in solution if the mixture is digested on a steam bath for twenty or thirty minutes. Another source of these three isotopes is the radon tubes discarded by hospitals giving radium treatments. One of these is ground in a mortar, dissolved in about two milliliters of hydrofluoric acid, and then made up to about 100 milliliters with 0.5 normal hydrochloric acid.

Ruthenium-106

0.1 molar ruthenium chloride

Ruthenium is obtained as the trichloride in an approximately six normal hydrochloric acid solution. This material will have carrier present but this carrier was not added during processing. The amount present will vary; therefore, the instructor should check the packing list for information on his particular lot. Since there will be insufficient carrier present to perform the experiment properly, the solution obtained should be added to the standard solution and the amount of carrier present may be disregarded.

Silver-111 [1]

0.01 molar silver nitrate
silver blocks plated with active silver

Radioactive silver may be obtained either in silver nitrate or carrier free in palladium metal. In order to prepare silver nitrate solution from the latter, the palladium metal is dissolved with fuming nitric acid and nine normal hydrochloric acid adding 100 milligrams of silver as a carrier. The solution is diluted and silver chloride precipitated with hydrochloric acid. Wash the chloride and redissolve in excess ammonium hydroxide. The silver is again precipitated as the sulfide with hydrogen sulfide, and the silver sulfide is redissolved, using hot nitric acid. Evaporate this solution to dryness, dissolve the residue in distilled water, and assay.

The required amount of this silver solution can be added to the inactive material to give a 0.01 normal silver nitrate solution.

The silver blocks should be plated using the silver cyanide process. The plating solution is prepared by precipitating the silver cyanide. This precipitate is dissolved in excess potassium cyanide. Pure silver should be used for both electrodes.

If the solid active silver nitrate is obtained, the preparation of the 0.01-molar solution may be prepared by dissolving the material in water and assaying. The plated blocks may be made from this material. It should be noted that the active silver obtained from palladium is apparently a pure beta emitter whereas that from the silver nitrate has both beta and gamma. This should be taken into consideration when this experiment is planned.

In preparing the electrolysis cell for Experiment XIV, a

[1] B. V. Rollin, *J. Am. Chem. Soc.* **62**, 86 (1940).

heavy coat of radioactive silver should be plated on the anode. The plating solution should be a portion of the silver nitrate solution (0.1 molar containing 35 to 50 microcuries of radiosilver per liter) employed as the electrolyte in the same experiment.

Sodium-24

0.01 molar sodium chloride

This material will be obtained as the solid and may be dissolved in water to give approximately a 0.01-molar solution. This may be diluted with standard sodium chloride solution in order to adjust the millicuries per liter to the desired value.

Sulfur-35

0.1 molar sulfuric acid

Sulfur-35 is available in several forms, depending upon its preparation at Oak Ridge National Laboratory. It may be obtained in two solid and two liquid forms. Of these only one seems advisable for the experiment to be performed. The two solid forms are elemental sulfur, one of which has had the major portion of the phosphorus-32 removed and the other will contain all the phosphorus. The two liquids differ in several respects. One liquid form is the sulfide dissolved in barium hydroxide. Carrier sulfur has been added to this material. The preparation is free of phosphorus-32; however sulfides in the low concentration as these solutions must be are very rapidly oxidized to sulfates by oxygen dissolved in the liquid and must, therefore, be stored under nitrogen. The presence of barium will precipitate any sulfate, thus making this material useless for the experiment described.

The sulfur-35 offered as sulfuric acid with no added carrier, even though at times it will contain small amounts of phosphorus, can be used. It should be remembered that the amount of phosphorus present will vary with the age of the solution (age being determined by the time since removal from the pile). The solution received can be diluted with 0.1-molar sulfuric acid to give the desired activity per liter.

Strontium-89

0.1 molar strontium nitrate

Radioactive strontium may be obtained in two forms (both solutions), depending entirely upon the ratio of the concentrations of strontium-89 and -90 that are present. It is desirable for the experiment outlined to obtain the material with the highest percentage of the 89 mass that is available. The strontium-90 emits low energy beta particles (0.6 Mev) when decaying to the active yttrium-90. The daughter element with the higher energy beta particles (2.5 Mev) will cause some difficulty during assay and in the experiment since it may not follow the strontium under all conditions. If certain precautions are taken during the experiment, it may be possible to use strontium-90 and measure the yttrium-90 activity in order to trace the strontium. The solutions are shipped in weak hydrochloric acid but with an activity sufficiently high that the small amount of hydrochloric acid present when added to the standard strontium solution will not affect the experiment.

Uranium

Uranyl nitrate
Uranium oxide (U_3O_8)

These materials are available in small quantities from chemical suppliers under specific conditions. The uranyl nitrate is dissolved in water to give the desired concentration or used as a solid depending upon the experiment.

Fifteen grams of uranium oxide is dissolved in the stoichiometric amount of concentrated nitric acid and the solution diluted to one liter.

Zinc

0.01-molar zinc nitrate solution

Radioactive zinc may be obtained as the metal which can be dissolved in nitric acid to produce the 0.01-molar zinc solution. Since insufficient zinc will be present to dilute the activity to the proper concentration, the foregoing solution should be diluted with a solution of standard inactive zinc.

Gamma Sandwich

The gamma sandwich is prepared so that gamma rays may be counted in the presence of betas by absorbing all the beta particles but allowing the gamma or the radiation produced by gamma rays to be counted. It is prepared by cementing together a sheet of aluminum (1,700 milligrams per square centimeter), a sheet of lead (2,000 milligrams per square centimeter), and a second sheet of aluminum on the top (200 milligrams per square centimeter). It is used in the same manner as other absorbers but the lighter (200 milligrams per square centimeter) aluminum must be nearest the Counter tube.

Ion Exchange. *Preparation of resin.*

The ion-exchange resin should be thoroughly wet with distilled water before placing the material in the column. If dry or partially dry resin is placed in the column, the expansion that occurs when the resin is moistened is likely to break the glass column violently. This is particularly true if the dry resin is moistened with hydrochloric acid.

In order to obtain the best results with ion exchange resins, the procedure that is to be used in this experiment should be followed several times before attempting to obtain data. That is, the cycle consisting of the medium from which the ion is to be absorbed and the eluant medium in the same relation as in the procedure should be passed through the column. (No activity should be used in any of the preparative solutions.)

APPENDIX 1

APPENDIX 2

Laboratory reports on each experiment should be turned into the instructor. They should include the following information:

1. *Title page.* Each report should have a title page giving the number and title of the experiment, the date performed, and the student's signature.

2. *Counting data.* All counting data should be recorded as the measurements are made. A suggested form for these sheets is illustrated in Figure 14. A place is provided at the bottom of the sheet for the instructor to sign before the student leaves the laboratory. A carbon copy is made as the measurements are recorded, and it is left on file in the laboratory.

3. *Counting data calculations.* Following the counting sheet, there should be a page of sample calculations. This will include an illustrative example of each different operation used in completing the data sheet.

4. *Calculations and questions.* Next on the report comes several pages making the calculations and answering the questions given at the end of each experiment.

5. *Discussion.* A brief discussion of the experiment should be presented, including the student's impressions, suggested improvements, sources of error, and other similar experiments that might be made.

6. *A safety report.* A brief summary of all safety measurements made and precautions taken during the experiment should be included.

If the student observes or is involved in any accident during the course of the laboratory period, a complete signed report must be included in the write up.

Each report should be neatly written or typed and bound in a suitable cover.

COUNTING DATA SHEET

No.	Time Begin	Time End	Count Time	Register Reading	Interpol. Reading	Total Counts	Back Ground	Dead Time Corr.	Corr. Count	Counts Min.	Std. Devn.
1	7 20	11 20	4 00	605	31	38751	124	820	37807	9452	49
2	11 20	61 20	50 00	40	1	2561	1550	0	1011	20.2	1.3

Instructor _____

Figure 14

APPENDIX 3

SURGICAL GLOVES

Wearing surgical gloves may be considered one of the best methods of hand protection. The advantages are: first, protection from direct hand contamination caused by handling contaminated equipment; and, second, the thickness of the rubber offers some protection by absorbing a part of the beta particles. However, the use of gloves does not permit the operator any leniency when working with active materials. He should consider the gloves as added protection.

In order to obtain the full value of surgical gloves certain techniques should be followed when putting on, removing, and storing them. Although many people dislike the gloves because the hands will perspire, this disadvantage, however, can be more than offset by the protection they offer. The reason for the perspiration is that the gloves must fit skin tight if they are to be truly useful. Loose fitting gloves are a hazard. The glove size should be as small as possible but not so small that the hand is cramped and normal movement of the fingers is not allowed.

If the gloves have been used previously, one should find them wrapped in tissue with the proper side out and the cuffs folded back approximately one inch. To put the gloves on, pick up one glove by the fold, being certain that the fingers grasp only the inside surface and slide the other hand into the glove. Next pick up the other glove by sliding the gloved fingers into the pocket formed by the folded cuff and then slip the glove over the hand. In this operation the gloved fingers must not touch the inside of the gloves. After both gloves are on, the cuffs may be rolled back and final adjustments made on the fingers. Extreme care must be exercised whenever gloves are put on or taken off that the outside of the glove does not touch the inside or that the bare fingers do not touch the outside.

Removal of the gloves is performed in a manner similar to putting them on. First, the gloved hands are thoroughly washed to remove all activity; they are dried and powdered with talc. Then the cuffs are folded back over the wrist, the gloved fingers slid into the fold, and the glove removed inside out. The inside of the second glove is grasped in the fingers and again removed inside out. The inside of the glove is dried. One must be careful to dry and powder the gloves thoroughly, otherwise any wet spots will tend to stick, causing difficulty the next time they are used. After powdering the inside of the gloves, they may be turned so that they are ready for immediate reuse. When doing this, push out the fingers and roll the palm back, always handling only the inside of the glove. Leave a portion of the cuff rolled so that only the inside of the glove is handled. If the gloves are to be stored, wrap each in tissue in order to protect the drawer in which they are kept.

Although this procedure may seem long and tedious, with practice the process is no more difficult than putting on any other pair of gloves; at the same time adequate protection is maintained. Needless to say if any pinholes appear in the gloves, they should be discarded immediately. Those who have used gloves have reverted, at times, to turning the glove by using air pressure or twisting the cuff and using the entrapped air to blow out the fingers. Although this is rapid it must be discouraged because any active particles on the gloves are usually blown into the air, thus producing an inhalation hazard.

APPENDIX 4

4—Quartz fiber electroscopes
4—Geiger-Mueller scalers
4—Time clocks for scalers
4—End-window Geiger-Mueller tubes, self-quenching
4—Cylindrical Geiger-Mueller tubes, self-quenching
4—Dipping Geiger-Mueller tubes, self-quenching
1—Radiation Monitor, Eck and Krebs tube
1—Radiation Monitor, thin-windowed end-window tube
2—Ionization chamber type monitors
10—Pen-type pocket ionization chambers
1—Charging and measuring instrument for pocket chambers
10—Film holders
8—Infrared drying lamps
16—100-lambda pipettes
1—Calibrated radioactivity reference source
2—Sets of absorbers
4—Precipitation set-ups
4—Ion exchange columns
4—Transference number apparatuses
4—Gamma sandwiches
4—Very short half-life wheels
50—Lead bricks
4—Metallic friction sliders
4—Hypodermic syringes and needles
2—Animal cages

Several types of liquid radioactivity apparatus
Blotting paper
"No-screen" X-ray film
Cellophane
Scotch tape
Several kinds and thicknesses of metal foil
Cardboard mounting cards

APPENDIX 5

A few of the many commercial organizations supplying equipment and materials useful in radiotracer work are listed below. The list is not complete and is meant only to be suggestive. Omission of a firm's name in no way implies that the products are, in the authors' opinion, inferior.

The numerals following a company's name indicate the articles that may be purchased from that company. The significance of the numbers is:

(1) Geiger-Mueller and similar counting tubes
(2) Scalers and amplifiers
(3) Survey and health instruments
(4) Radiolaboratory accessories
(5) Electroscopes
(6) Electrometers
(7) Radioactivity standards
(8) Specially prepared radioactive compounds

1. Applied Physics Corporation .... (6)
   40 South Oak Knoll
   Pasadena 1, California

2. Atomic Instrument Company .... (2, 3)
   160 Charles Street
   Boston 14, Massachusetts

3. Cambridge Instrument Company .... (6)
   72 East Forty-sixth Street
   New York, New York

4. Cyclotron Specialties Company .... (1, 2)
   Moraga 8, California

5. El-tronics, Incorporated .... (1, 2, 3)

1920 Lincoln-Liberty Building
Philadelphia 7, Pennsylvania

6. Geophysical Instrument Company .... (1, 2, 3, 4)
Key Boulevard and Nash Street
Arlington, Virginia

7. Fred C. Henson Company .... (3, 5)
3511 East Colorado Street
Pasadena, California

8. Herback and Rademan Company .... (1, 2, 3)
517 Ludlow Street
Philadelphia 6, Pennsylvania

9. The Kelley-Koett Manufacturing Company .... (1, 2, 3)
Covington, Kentucky

10. National Technical Laboratory .... (3, 6)
820 Mission Street
South Pasadena, California

11. Newman Metal Products Manufacturing
Company .... (3, film badges)
126 South Clinton Street
Chicago 6, Illinois

12. North American Phillips Company .... (1, 3)
100 East Forty-second Street
New York 17, New York

13. Nuclear Instrument and Chemical Corpora-
tion .... (1, 2, 3, 4)
223 West Erie Street
Chicago 10, Illinois

14. Radiation Counter Laboratories .... (1, 2, 3, 4, 7)
1844 West Twenty-first Street
Chicago 8, Illinois

15. Technical Associates .... (1, 2, 3, 4)
3730 San Fernando Road
Glendale 4, California

16. Texas Research Foundation .... (8)
Renner, Texas

17. Tracerlab, Incorporated .... (1, 2, 3, 4, 7, 8)
55 Oliver Street
Boston 10, Massachusetts

18. Victoreen Instrument Company .... (1, 2, 3)
5806 Hough Avenue
Cleveland 3, Ohio

APPENDIX 6

SCALE OF 64

	0	1	2	3	4	5	6	7	8	9
0	00000	00064	00128	00192	00256	00320	00384	00448	00512	00576
1	00640	00704	00768	00832	00896	00960	01024	01088	01152	01216
2	01280	01344	01408	01472	01536	01600	01664	01728	01792	01856
3	01920	01984	02048	02112	02176	02240	02304	02368	02432	02496
4	02560	02624	02688	02752	02816	02880	02844	03008	03072	03136
5	03200	03264	03328	03392	03456	03520	03584	03648	03712	03776
6	03840	03904	03968	04032	04096	04160	04224	04288	04352	04416
7	04480	04544	04608	04672	04736	04800	04864	04928	04992	05056
8	05120	05184	05248	05312	05376	05440	05504	05568	05632	05696
9	05760	05724	05888	05952	06016	06080	06144	06208	06272	06336
10	06400	06464	06526	06592	06656	06720	06784	06848	06912	06976
11	07040	07104	07168	07232	07296	07360	07424	07488	07552	07616
12	07680	07744	07808	07872	07936	08000	08064	08128	08192	08256
13	08320	08384	08448	08512	08576	08640	08704	08768	08832	08896
14	08960	09024	09088	09152	09216	09280	09344	09408	09472	09536
15	09600	09664	09728	09792	09856	09920	09984	10048	10112	10176
16	10240	10304	10368	10432	10496	10560	10624	10688	10752	10816
17	10880	10944	11008	11072	11136	11200	11264	11328	11392	11456
18	11520	11584	11648	11712	11776	11840	11904	11968	12032	12096
19	12160	12224	12288	12352	12416	12480	12544	12608	12672	12736
20	12800	12864	12928	12992	13056	13120	13184	13248	13312	13376
21	13440	13504	13568	13632	13696	13760	13824	13888	13952	14016
22	14080	14144	14208	14272	14336	14400	14464	14528	14592	14656
23	14720	14784	14848	14912	14976	15040	15104	15168	15232	15296
24	15360	15424	15488	15552	15616	15680	15744	15808	15872	15936
25	16000	16064	16128	16192	16256	16320	16384	16448	16512	16576
26	16640	16704	16768	16832	16896	16960	17024	17088	17152	17216
27	17280	17344	17408	17472	17536	17600	17664	17728	17792	17856
28	17920	17984	18048	18112	18176	18240	18304	18368	18432	18496
29	18560	18624	18688	18752	18816	18880	18944	19008	19072	19136
30	19200	19264	19328	19392	19456	19520	19584	19648	19712	19776
31	19840	19904	19968	20032	20096	20160	20224	20288	20352	20416
32	20480	20544	20608	20672	20736	20800	20864	20928	20992	21056
33	20020	21184	21248	21312	21376	21440	21504	21568	21632	21696
34	21760	21824	21888	21952	22016	22080	22144	22208	22272	22336
35	22400	22464	22528	22592	22656	22720	22784	22848	22912	22976

	0	1	2	3	4	5	6	7	8	9
36	23040	23104	23168	23232	23296	23360	23424	23488	23552	23616
37	23680	23744	23808	23872	23946	24000	24064	24128	24192	24256
38	24320	24384	24448	24512	24576	24640	24704	24768	24832	24896
39	24960	25024	25088	25152	25216	25280	25344	25408	25472	25536
40	25600	25664	25728	25792	25856	25920	25984	26048	26112	26176
41	26240	26304	26368	26432	26496	26560	26624	26688	26752	26816
42	26880	26944	27008	27072	27136	27200	27264	27328	27392	27456
43	27520	27584	27648	27712	27776	27840	27904	27968	28032	28096
44	28160	28224	28288	28352	28416	28480	28544	28608	28672	28736
45	28800	28864	28928	28992	29056	29120	29184	29248	29312	29376
46	29440	29504	29568	29632	29696	29760	29824	29888	29952	30016
47	30080	30144	30208	30272	30336	30400	30464	30528	30592	30656
48	30720	30784	30848	30912	30976	31040	31104	31168	31232	31296
49	31360	31424	31488	31552	31616	31680	31744	31808	31872	31936
50	32000	32064	32128	32192	32256	32320	32384	32448	32512	32576
51	32640	32704	32768	32832	32896	32960	33024	33088	33152	33216
52	33280	33344	33408	33472	33536	33600	33664	33728	33792	33856
53	33920	33984	34048	34112	34176	34240	34304	34368	34432	34496
54	34560	34624	34688	34752	34816	34880	34944	35008	35072	35136
55	35200	35264	35328	35392	35456	35520	35584	35648	35712	35776
56	35840	35904	35968	36032	36096	36160	36224	36288	36352	36416
57	36480	36544	36608	36672	36736	36800	36864	36928	36992	37056
58	37120	37184	37248	37312	37376	37400	37504	37568	37632	37696
59	37760	37824	37888	37952	38016	38080	38144	38208	38272	38332
60	38400	38464	38528	38592	38656	38720	38784	38848	38912	38976
61	39040	39104	39168	39232	39296	39360	39424	39488	39552	39616
62	39680	39744	39808	39872	39936	40000	40064	40128	40192	40256
63	40320	40384	40448	40512	40576	40640	40704	40768	40832	40896
64	40960	41024	41088	41152	41216	41280	41344	41408	41472	41536
65	41600	41664	41728	41792	41856	41920	41984	42048	42112	42176
66	42240	42304	42368	42432	42496	42560	42624	42688	42752	42816
67	42880	42944	43008	43072	43136	43200	43264	43328	43392	43456
68	43520	43584	43648	43712	43776	43840	43904	43968	44032	44096
69	44160	44224	44288	44352	44416	44480	44544	44608	44672	44736
70	44800	44864	44928	44992	45056	45120	45184	45248	45312	45376
71	45440	45504	45568	45632	45696	45760	45824	45888	45952	46016
72	46080	46144	46208	46272	46336	46400	46464	46528	46592	46656
73	46720	46784	46848	46912	46976	47040	47104	47168	47232	47296
74	47360	47424	47488	47552	47616	47680	47744	47808	47872	47936
75	48000	48064	48128	48192	48256	48320	48384	48448	48512	48576
76	48640	48704	48768	48832	48896	48960	49024	49088	49152	49216
77	49280	49344	49408	49472	49536	49600	49664	49728	49792	49856
78	49920	49984	50048	50112	50176	50240	50304	50368	50432	50496
79	50560	50624	50688	50752	50816	50880	50944	51008	51072	51136
80	51200	51264	51328	51392	51456	51520	51584	51648	51812	51776

	0	1	2	3	4	5	6	7	8	9
81	51840	51904	51968	52032	52096	52160	52224	52288	52352	52416
82	52480	52544	52608	52672	52736	52800	52864	52928	52992	53056
83	53120	53184	53248	53312	53376	53440	53504	53568	53632	53696
84	53760	53824	53888	53952	54016	54080	54144	54208	54272	54336
85	54400	54464	54528	54592	54656	54720	54784	54848	54912	54976
86	55040	55104	55168	55232	55296	55360	55424	55488	55552	55616
87	55680	55744	55808	55872	55936	56000	56064	56128	56192	56256
88	56320	56384	56448	56512	56576	56640	56704	56768	56832	56896
89	56960	57024	57088	57152	57216	57280	57344	57408	57472	57536
90	57600	57664	57728	57792	57856	57920	57984	58048	58112	58176
91	58240	58304	58368	58432	58496	58560	58624	58688	58752	58816
92	58880	58944	59008	59072	59136	59200	59264	59328	59392	59456
93	59520	59584	59648	59712	59776	59840	59904	59968	60032	60096
94	60160	60224	60288	60352	60416	60480	60544	60608	60672	60736
95	60800	60864	60928	60992	61056	61120	61184	61248	61312	61376
96	61440	61504	61568	61632	61696	61760	61824	61888	61952	62016
97	62080	62144	62208	62272	62336	62400	62464	62528	62592	62656
98	62720	62784	62848	62912	62976	63040	63104	63168	63232	63296
99	63360	63424	63488	63552	63616	63680	63744	63808	63872	63936
100	64000	64064	64128	64192	64256	64320	64384	64448	64512	64576

SCALE OF 32

	0	1	2	3	4	5	6	7	8	9
0	00000	00032	00064	00096	00128	00160	00192	00224	00256	00288
1	00320	00352	00384	00416	00448	00480	00512	00544	00576	00608
2	00640	00672	00704	00736	00768	00800	00832	00864	00896	00928
3	00960	00992	01024	01056	01088	01120	01152	01184	01216	01248
4	01280	01312	01344	01376	01408	01440	01472	01504	01536	01568
5	01600	01632	01664	01696	01728	01760	01792	01824	01856	01888
6	01920	01952	01984	02016	02048	02080	02112	02144	02176	02208
7	02240	02272	02304	02336	02368	02400	02432	02464	02496	02528
8	02560	02592	02624	02656	02688	02720	02752	02784	02816	02848
9	02880	02912	02944	02976	03008	03040	03072	03104	03136	03168
10	03200	03232	03264	03296	03328	03360	03392	03424	03456	03488
11	03520	03552	03584	03616	03648	03680	03712	03744	03776	03808
12	03840	03872	03904	03936	03968	04000	04032	04064	04096	04128
13	04160	04192	04224	04256	04288	04320	04352	04384	04416	04448
14	04480	04512	04544	04576	04608	04640	04672	04704	04736	04768
15	04800	04832	04864	04896	04928	04960	04992	05024	05056	05088
16	05120	05152	05184	05216	05248	05280	05312	05344	05376	05408
17	05440	05472	05504	05536	05568	05600	05632	05664	05696	05728
18	05760	05792	05824	05856	05888	05920	05952	059?4	06016	06048
19	06080	06112	06144	06176	06208	06240	06272	06304	06336	06368
20	06400	06432	06464	06496	06528	06560	06592	06624	06656	06688

	0	1	2	3	4	5	6	7	8	9
21	06720	06752	06784	06816	06848	06880	06912	06944	06976	07008
22	07040	07072	07104	07136	07168	07200	07232	07264	07296	07328
23	07360	07392	07424	07456	07488	07520	07552	07584	07616	07648
24	07680	07712	07744	07776	07808	07840	07872	07904	07936	07968
25	08000	08032	08064	08096	08128	08160	08192	08224	08256	08288
26	08320	08352	08384	08416	08448	08480	08512	08544	08576	08608
27	08640	08672	08704	08736	08768	08800	08832	08864	08896	08928
28	08960	08992	09024	09056	09088	09120	09152	09184	09216	09248
29	09280	09312	09344	09376	09418	09440	09472	09504	09536	09568
30	09600	09632	09664	09696	09728	09760	09792	09824	09856	09888
31	09920	09952	09984	10016	10048	10080	10112	10144	10176	10208
32	10240	10272	10304	10336	10368	10400	10432	10464	10496	10528
33	10560	10592	10624	10656	10688	10720	10752	10784	10816	10848
34	10880	10912	10944	10976	11008	11040	11072	11104	11136	11168
35	11200	11232	11264	11296	11328	11360	11392	11424	11456	11488
36	11520	11552	11584	11616	11648	11680	11712	11744	11776	11808
37	11840	11872	11904	11936	11968	12000	12032	12064	12096	12128
38	12160	12192	12224	12256	12288	12320	12352	12384	12416	12448
39	12480	12512	12544	12576	12608	12640	12672	12704	12736	12768
40	12800	12832	12864	12896	12928	12960	12992	13024	13056	13088
41	13120	13152	13184	13216	13248	13280	13312	13344	13376	13408
42	14330	13472	13504	13536	13568	13600	13632	13664	13696	13728
43	13760	13792	13824	13856	13888	13920	13952	13984	14016	14048
44	14080	14112	14144	14176	14208	14240	14272	14304	14336	14368
45	14400	14432	14464	14496	14528	14560	14592	14624	14656	14688
46	14720	14752	14784	14816	14848	14880	14912	14944	14976	15008
47	15040	15072	15104	15136	15168	15200	15232	15264	15296	15328
48	15360	15392	15424	15456	15488	15520	15552	15584	15616	15648
49	15680	15712	15744	15776	15808	15840	15872	15904	15936	15968
50	16000	16032	16064	16096	16128	16160	16192	16224	16256	16288
51	16320	16352	16384	16416	16448	16480	16512	16544	16576	16608
52	16640	16672	16704	16736	16768	16800	16832	16864	16896	16928
53	16960	16992	17024	17056	17088	17120	17152	17184	17216	17248
54	17280	17312	17344	17376	17408	17440	17472	17504	17536	17568
55	17600	17632	17664	17696	17728	17760	17792	17824	17856	17888
56	17920	17952	17984	18016	18048	18080	18112	18144	18176	18208
57	18240	18272	18304	18336	18368	18400	18432	18464	18496	18528
58	18560	18592	18624	18656	18688	18720	18752	18784	18816	18848
59	18880	18912	18944	18976	19008	19040	19072	19104	19136	19168
60	19200	19232	19264	19296	19328	19360	19392	19424	19456	19488
61	19520	19552	19584	19616	19648	19630	19712	19744	19776	19808
62	19840	19872	19904	19936	19968	20000	20032	20064	20096	20128
63	20160	20192	20224	20256	20288	20320	20352	20384	20416	20448
64	20480	20512	20544	20576	20608	20640	20672	20704	20736	20768
65	20800	20832	20864	20896	20928	20960	20992	21024	21056	21088

	0	1	2	3	4	5	6	7	8	9
66	21120	21152	21184	21216	21248	21280	21312	21344	21376	21408
67	21440	21472	21504	21536	21568	21600	21632	21664	21696	21728
68	21760	21792	21824	21856	21888	21920	21952	21984	22016	22048
69	22080	22112	22144	22176	22208	22240	22272	22304	22336	22368
70	22400	22432	22464	22496	22528	22560	22592	22624	22656	22688
71	22720	22752	22784	22816	22848	22880	22912	22944	22976	23008
72	23040	23072	23104	23136	23168	23200	23232	23264	23296	23328
73	23360	23392	23424	23456	23488	23520	23552	23584	23616	23648
74	23680	23712	23744	23776	23808	23840	23872	23904	23836	23968
75	24000	24032	24064	24096	24128	24160	24192	24224	24256	24288
76	24320	24352	24384	24416	24448	24480	24512	24544	24576	24608
77	24640	24672	24704	24736	24768	24800	24832	24864	24896	24928
78	24960	24992	25024	25056	25088	25120	25152	25184	25216	25248
79	25280	25312	25344	25376	25408	25440	25472	25504	25536	25568
80	25600	25632	25664	25696	25728	25760	25792	25824	25856	25888
81	25920	25952	25984	26016	26048	26080	26112	26144	26176	26208
82	26240	26272	26304	26336	26368	26400	26432	26464	26496	26528
83	26560	26592	26624	26656	26688	26720	26752	26784	26816	26848
84	26880	26912	26944	26976	27008	27040	27072	27104	27136	27168
85	27200	27232	27264	27296	27328	27360	27392	27424	27456	27488
86	27520	27552	27584	27616	27648	27680	27712	27744	27776	27808
87	27840	27872	27904	27936	27968	28000	28032	28064	28096	28128
88	28160	28192	28224	28256	28288	28320	28352	28384	28416	28448
89	28480	28512	28544	28576	28608	28640	28672	28704	28736	28768
90	28800	28832	28864	28896	28928	28960	28992	29024	29056	29088
91	29120	29152	29184	29216	29248	29280	29312	29344	29376	29408
92	29440	29472	29504	29536	29568	29600	29632	29664	29696	29728
93	29760	29792	29824	29856	29888	29920	29952	29984	30016	30048
94	30080	30112	30144	30176	30208	30240	30272	30304	30336	30368
95	30400	30432	30464	30496	30528	30560	30592	30624	30656	30688
96	30720	30752	30784	30816	30848	30880	30912	30944	30976	31008
97	31040	31072	31104	31136	31168	31200	31232	31264	31296	31328
98	31360	31392	31424	31456	31488	31520	31552	31584	31616	31648
99	31680	31712	31744	31776	31808	31840	31872	31904	31936	31968
100	32000	32032	32064	32096	32128	32160	32192	32224	32256	32288

APPENDIX 7

SOME RADIOISOTOPES OF TRACER INTEREST

Z	Element	A	Mass	% Abund.	$t_{\frac{1}{2}}$	Radiation Energies β	γ	Decay Prod.
0	electron	0	0.000548					
0	neutron	1	1.00893					
1	proton	1	1.007582					
2	alpha	4	4.002764					
4	Be	9	9.01486	100				
6	C	11	11.01499		$8.8s$	3.4		$^{11}_{5}B$
6	C	14	14.0078		$5700y$	0.145		$^{14}_{7}N$
11	Na	24	23.99774		$14.8h$	1.4	1.38	$^{24}_{12}Mg$
							3.73	
15	P	32	31.9841		$14.3d$	1.69		$^{32}_{16}S$
16	S	35			$87.1d$	0.17		$^{35}_{17}Cl$
19	K	40	39.975	0.011	$4 \times 10^{8}y$	0.4	2.0	$^{40}_{20}Ca$
						0.7	K	
20	Ca	45	44.97075		$180d$	0.2		$^{45}_{21}Sc$
26	Fe	55			$4y$		0.09	$^{55}_{25}Mn$
							K	
26	Fe	59			$44d$	0.26	1.3	$^{59}_{27}Co$
						0.46	1.1	
27	Co	60			$5.3y$	0.31	1.1	$^{60}_{28}Ni$
30	Zn	65			$250d$	0.4	1.14	$^{65}_{29}Cu$
							K	
35	Br	80			$4.5h$		0.49	$^{80}_{35}Br^{*}$
							0.37	
							IT	
35	Br	80			$18m$	2.0	0.5	$^{80}_{36}Kr$
35	Br	82			$34h$	0.465	0.56	$^{82}_{36}Kr$
							0.79	

Z	Element	A	Mass	% Abund.	$t_{\frac{1}{2}}$	Radiation Energies β	γ	Decay Prod.
							1.35	
38	Sr	89			53d	1.5		$^{89}_{39}\text{Y}$
38	Sr	90			25y	0.6		$^{90}_{39}\text{Y*}$
39	Y	90			65h	2.5		$^{90}_{40}\text{Zr}$
44	Ru	106			1y	0.03		$^{106}_{45}\text{Rh*}$
45	Rh	106			30s	2.8		$^{106}_{46}\text{Pd}$
						4.5		
47	Ag	111			7.5d	1.0		$^{111}_{48}\text{Cd}$
53	I	131			8.0d	0.69	0.36	$^{131}_{54}\text{Xe}$
90	Th (UX₁)	234			24.5d	0.12	0.09	$^{234}_{91}\text{Pa*}$
						0.30		
91	Pa (UX₂)	234			1.14m	2.32	0.8	$^{234}_{92}\text{U*}$

APPENDIX 8

Fundamental Constants

Electronic

Charge of electron .... $(4.8021 \pm 0.0006) \times 10^{-10}$ esu
Mass of electron .... $(9.1066 \pm 0.0032) \times 10^{-28}$ g
Atomic Weight of electron .. 0.0005486

Atomic

Mass of hydrogen atom .... $(1.67339 \pm 0.00031) \times 10^{-24}$ g
Avogadro's Number (N) .... $(6.02338 \pm 0.00043) \times 10^{23}$/g mol

Energy

1 electron volt (ev) .... 1.60×10^{-6} ergs
$\qquad\qquad\qquad\qquad\quad 1.07 \times 10^{-9}$ mass units
1 million electron volts
(Mev) .... 10^6 ev
1 atomic mass unit (amu) .... 931 Mev
1 ion pair in air .... 32.5 ev

Radiation

Planck's constant (h) .... $(6.624 \pm 0.002) \times 10^{-27}$ erg sec
Speed of light .... $(2.99776 \pm 0.00004) \times 10^{10}$ cm/sec
1 curie (c) .... 3.7×10^{10} dis/sec
$\qquad\qquad\qquad\qquad\quad 2.22 \times 10^{12}$ dis/min
1 millicurie (mc) .... 10^{-3} curie
1 microcurie (μc) .... 10^{-6} curie
1 rutherford (rd) .... 1.00×10^6 dis/sec
$\qquad\qquad\qquad\qquad\quad 6.00 \times 10^7$ dis/min
$\qquad\qquad\qquad\qquad\quad$ 1/37 millicurie
1 roentgen (r) .... 1 esu/cc std air
$\qquad\qquad\qquad\qquad\quad 2.083 \times 10^9$ ion pairs/cc std air
$\qquad\qquad\qquad\qquad\quad 6.77 \times 10^4$ Mev/cc std air

INDEX